W9-AYD-079

W O R D S M I T H
A P P R E N T I C E

WRITING EXCELLENCE

THROUGH UNIQUE,

SKILL-BUILDING EXERCISES

FOR GRADES 4 - 6

by

Janie B. Cheaney

Illustrated by Tielman D. Cheaney

This copy of *WORDSMITH APPRENTICE* belongs to

_____

Name

_____

Date

Copyright 1995 by J.B. Cheaney

Published by **DGC Inc.**, Humansville, Missouri

Distributed by

Common Sense Press

See where learning takes you.

8786 Highway 21 • Melrose, FL 32666
(352) 475-5757 • Fax: (352) 475-6105

ABOUT THE AUTHOR: Janie Cheaney is a wife since 1971, a mother since 1975, and a homeschool teacher since 1985. She is the author of Wordsmith: A Creative Writing Course for Young People, as well as numerous articles, stories and plays. She lives in the Ozarks of Missouri with her family.

ABOUT THE ILLUSTRATOR: Tielman Cheaney, age 16, has been homeschooled since the middle of his first grade year. He has always shown an interest in and a talent for drawing and design. His medium is pen and ink, his style is dramatic and humorous, and his ambition is to be an animator for Walt Disney Studios.

TABLE OF CONTENTS

TO THE TEACHER..i
    1. APPROACH AND SCOPE..i
    2. OUTLINE i
    3. HOW TO USE **WORDSMITH APPRENTICE**......................iii

INTRODUCTION 1
    1. TO THE STUDENT...1
    2. *EDITOR'S DESK* (Comic) *-INTRODUCTION* 2
    3. TOUR OF THE NEWSPAPER...3
    4. WRITING IS ESSENTIAL 4
    5. "EMPLOYMENT APPLICATION"...4
    6. IMAGINATION STRETCHER 6

PART I: NOUNS, VERBS & BASIC SENTENCE STRUCTURE 7

EDITOR'S DESK - NOUNS..8
1: NOUNS ARE KEY 9
    List Mania 9
    Specific Nouns Preferred 11
    Classified Ads 13
    Poetry 14
EDITOR'S DESK - VERBS 17
2: VERBS VITAL..18
    Verbs Wanted 20
    Vivid Verbs..22
    Linking Verbs..23
EDITOR'S DESK - BASIC SENTENCE STRUCTURE 25
3: SENTENCES MAKE SENSE 26
    Sentence Form 26
    Compound Sentences 28
4. FOUR SENTENCE TYPES..29
    Declarative Sentences...29
    Interrogative Sentences...29
    Imperative Sentences..30
    Exclamatory Sentences...31
5. CAPTION WRITING 32
6. YOU ARE INVITED 33
7. LETTER WRITING..34
8. HEADLINES...36

(continued on next page)

PART II: MODIFIERS & MORE COMPLEX SENTENCES 39

EDITOR'S DESK - ADJECTIVES AND ADVERBS 40
1. MODIFIERS COMPLETE SENTENCES 41
   Adjectives 41
   Adverbs 43
2. MODIFIERS ARE FUN 45
   Mystery Sacks 45
   Word Portraits 45
   "Tom Swifties" 46
   Crossword Puzzles 47
3. WORDS AND WEATHER 49
EDITOR'S DESK - PREPOSITIONS 51
4. PREPOSITIONS 52
   Family Photos 53
   Practice Makes Perfect 55
5. SENTENCE REVIEW 57
6. EDITORS AID REPORTERS 58
7. ADVERTISING 59
8. REAL ESTATE BOOM 62
9. EXOTIC DESTINATIONS 65
10. READING REVIEWERS 68

PART III: ORGANIZING AND REPORTING 71

EDITOR'S DESK - WHAT IS A PARAGRAPH? 72
1. PARAGRAPHS 73
   Paragraph Principles 73
   Editing Paragraphs 74
2. WRITERS AT HOME 78
3. SYNOPSIS SPECIALISTS 84
4. CONTEST TIME 87
EDITOR'S DESK - WHO, WHAT WHEN, WHERE, WHY, HOW 89
5. REPORTING 90
   Buzzing Around Town 90
   News Briefs 92
   News Stories Close to Home 95
6. FASCINATING FUNNIES (DIALOGUE) 97
7. PRACTICE YOUR "HOOK" (OPENING STATEMENT) 100
8. REPORTERS FILL IN THE BLANKS 103
9. INVESTIGATING 107
10. OPINION WRITING 113
   New Face On Op-Ed Page 113
   How To Write an Editorial 116
11. NEW CHALLENGES 118

ANSWERS .... A & B

TO THE TEACHER

About our philosophy:

Writing is one of the most basic skills anyone will ever learn, and learning to write goes hand-in-hand with learning to think. To organize information, recall details, and get right to the point are hallmarks of good writing *and* clear thinking. It's no wonder that verbal scores count for twice as many points as math scores on standardized tests. The ability to work with words and the ideas behind them is absolutely vital to *any* kind of academic learning and vocation.

My own experience with teaching writing to children is that some love it from the start, but most don't. A common misconception is that writing (especially "creative" writing) is a special gift that can't be taught. Wrong! If that suspicion is lurking in your mind, you will be ahead of the game if you understand this simple fact: *Writing is a craft.* Any craft can be taught. How does one learn? By learning how to use the tools, mastering the techniques, and practicing. Of course, it helps if the student brings some enthusiasm to the task. **Wordsmith Apprentice** attempts to arouse that enthusiasm and build those vital skills.

About the approach:

The intermediate grades (4th, 5th and 6th) are the ideal time to become familiar with the "tools" of writing: words, sentences, and paragraphs. Since use improves with practice, students should have plenty of opportunities to use their tools. But there's the rub for many of us parents. Grammar-book exercises, we've found, are not applicable to our unique child's experience, and the skills apparently mastered on the model sentences don't carry over to actual writing projects. Creative writing projects for beginners should meet three criteria: they should be firmly rooted in the writer's experience, they should build on skills already learned while stretching to new ones, and they should be at least a little fun.

Wordsmith Apprentice meets these criteria within the framework of journalism. The scenario of writing for a small-town weekly newspaper introduces an element of imagination that makes the writing projects fun and interesting while at the same time it reinforces practical skills.

About the Scope:

Your student joins the "staff" of an unnamed newspaper. The "editor" provides instruction on fundamentals of writing according to the following outline:

PART ONE. NOUNS, VERBS AND BASIC SENTENCE STRUCTURE. This section introduces five parts of speech: *nouns, verbs, articles, pronouns* and *conjunctions.* If these terms are totally new, some supplementary grammar work will probably be needed. The focus in this section is not so much on what these words *are* as how they are *used* in a sentence. *Articles* are introduced with *nouns* as "noun markers," *pronouns* as noun substitutes. The *verb* category includes action, linking and helping verbs. *Conjunctions* are introduced in connection with sentence structure.

WRITING PROJECTS IN PART ONE:
    Application for employment
    "For Sale" ads
    "Help Wanted" ads
    Haiku poetry
    Sports (action-verb) poetry
    Writing definitions
    Four-sentence captions
    Invitations
    Thank-you notes
    Headlines
    Various "Imagination Stretchers" throughout

[Please Note: Understanding basic sentence structure is vital to learning to write, so you may need to have your student repeat some or all of the PART ONE exercises before proceeding to PART TWO.]

PART TWO. MODIFIERS AND MORE COMPLEX SENTENCES. Nouns and verbs (or their substitutes) <u>always</u> lay the foundation of a sentence. Everything else is a modifier attached to the subject, verb or object. PART TWO addresses three types of modifiers: *adjectives, adverbs* and *prepositional phrases* (another type of modifier, the *clause*, is usually not introduced until 6th grade).

WRITING PROJECTS IN PART TWO:
    Word games and puzzles
    Display advertising
    Expanded captions
    Editing
    Travel writing
    Book reviews
    Various "Imaginations Stretchers" throughout

PART THREE. ORGANIZING AND REPORTING. Once a student feels comfortable with the basics of sentence structure, it's time to learn how to organize those sentences in a logical fashion. That's what paragraphing is all about. The student gains experience in recognizing a topic sentence, writing in sequence and summarizing the main points. With a grasp on these principles, he or she is ready to move on to reporting and the "five W's." Answering the Who, What, When Where and Why questions gives the student a flexible framework for writing simple reports, stories, even letters. Beginning writers usually need some such outline to help them get started, and the old journalism standby (the "five W's") works remarkably well with all kinds of writing assignments, "creative" or not.

WRITING PROJECTS IN PART THREE:
    Recipes
    Household hints
    Program synopses
    News briefs
    Comics (dialogue)
    Sports stories
    News articles

(continued on next page)

Editorials
Various "Imagination Stretchers" throughout

HOW TO USE **WORDSMITH APPRENTICE**

The purpose of the course is to awaken students to the fascinating possibilities of language and imagination while they learn solid principles of writing structure, content and organization. The course allows plenty of opportunity for a teacher to be involved by responding to the child's work, offering suggestions when asked, or even doing some of the exercises along with the student.

In these early attempts at creative writing, children need encouragement more than iron discipline. That's not to say that grammatical or spelling errors should not be corrected, but revision needn't play so large a role in the writing process as it will later.

The book is not divided into "lessons" so much as topics. It will be up to you how many pages to cover in a week or a day. Many fourth-graders will be enthusiastic about the course until they bog down in basic sentence structure, say, or prepositional phrases. If they come to a point where **Wordsmith Apprentice** is more pain than gain, it might be wise to lay the book aside for a couple of months while they gain more proficiency in grammar.

On the other hand, some children will steam right through the book and beg for more. These literary wonders may be excited by the prospect of editing their own newspaper. It's hard to imagine a project more conducive to developing writing skills.

The student will need a spiral notebook for some of the writing assignments and any additional projects inspired by the book.

Answers for some of the exercises are found on pages A & B at the end of this workbook. You may remove or leave them, whichever you feel is best.

Two supplementary resources will be very helpful to this course. One is a thesaurus (specifically called for in a few exercises). Paperback copies of *Roget's Thesaurus* are easily available at any bookstore, but no teacher should overlook the editions that are written especially for children. One of these is *A First Thesaurus*, by Harriet Wittels and Joan Greisman.

The other resource is a newspaper. Big-city newspapers are best, simply because of the greater variety of material in them. I realize that some of this material is not appropriate for children, and the skepticism that many parents share about the mainstream media is justified. Still, it will be very instructive to use a few newspapers as references throughout this course. If you do not subscribe to a newspaper, I suggest you buy one Sunday edition, one Saturday and one daily. These three will last you through the entire course--the news doesn't have to be new!

Once your student has finished **Wordsmith Apprentice**, the next logical step is **Wordsmith: A Creative Writing Course for Young People**. This book (geared to the junior high grades) takes a more disciplined approach to specific writing projects, makes use of the adolescent propensity toward introspection to produce more thoughtful, personal work, and provides increased confidence through blossoming writing skills.

TO THE STUDENT

Writing is one of the most important skills you will ever learn. Whether you like it or not, at times in your life you will be called upon to express your thoughts in writing. Just suppose:

You are asked why you want a certain job.

You want to send your mother a special birthday or holiday greeting.

Your local hang-gliding club volunteers you to write the club history.

Your boss demands a report on sewing needle factories in South America (due tomorrow).

You are called upon to teach a Sunday school class.

You want to convince someone to marry you.

All of these will be much easier if you know how to write down your own thoughts.

Have you ever tried to play a violin? It looks easy, but when you pick up the instrument and draw the bow across its strings, the sound that comes out is not at all what you hoped to hear! If you want to play you'll have to learn how. A teacher can show you where to put your fingers and how to handle the bow, and of course you must practice. You'll start with simple tunes like "Twinkle, Twinkle, Little Star," then go on to more complicated ones as your skills improve.

We learn to write the same way: by learning the skills of writing and then practicing them. By going slowly, step by step and year by year, we become writers.

This book will help you get started on the road to becoming a writer. To make the "journey" more interesting, we'll pretend that you have gone to work for a small town newspaper.

Newspaper work involves all kinds of writing, from very simple to very complex. Besides this book you will need an ordinary spiral notebook and several pencils. You should also keep a Sunday and weekday copy of your local newspaper nearby because you will be using them for reference.

We'll start with little jobs like classified ads, picture captions, and "fillers." You will practice writing complete sentences, then use them in advertising, book reviews and recipes. When you become a "staff reporter" you'll be ready to write news stories and editorials.

But first things first. Let's meet the editor of our newspaper.

A TOUR OF THE NEWSPAPER

Newspapers are divided into sections dealing with different kinds of "news." The larger the newspaper, the more sections it will have. Most newspapers follow a general pattern like the one below.

All these departments are included in our paper. During the time you'll be working with us, you can expect to get at least a little experience in most of them.

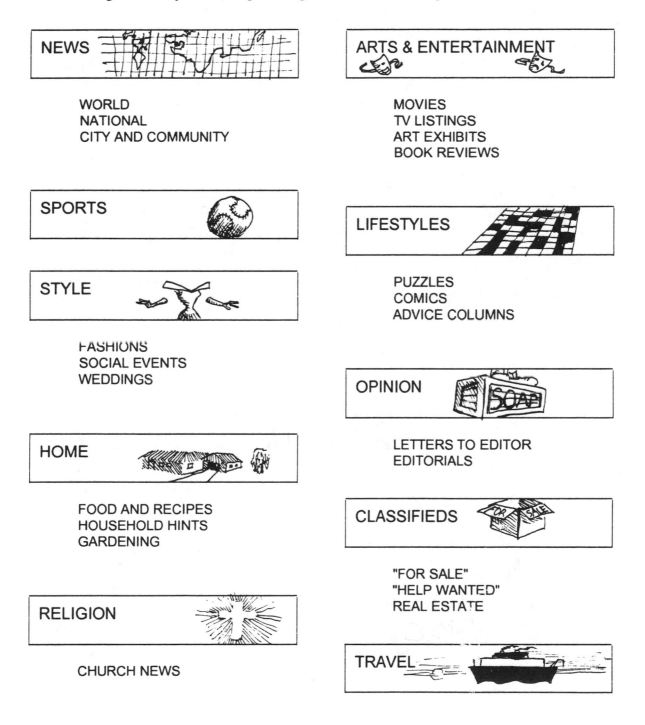

NEWS

WORLD
NATIONAL
CITY AND COMMUNITY

ARTS & ENTERTAINMENT

MOVIES
TV LISTINGS
ART EXHIBITS
BOOK REVIEWS

SPORTS

STYLE

FASHIONS
SOCIAL EVENTS
WEDDINGS

LIFESTYLES

PUZZLES
COMICS
ADVICE COLUMNS

OPINION

LETTERS TO EDITOR
EDITORIALS

HOME

FOOD AND RECIPES
HOUSEHOLD HINTS
GARDENING

CLASSIFIEDS

"FOR SALE"
"HELP WANTED"
REAL ESTATE

RELIGION

CHURCH NEWS

TRAVEL

WRITING IS ESSENTIAL, EDITOR CLAIMS

As our editor said, writing is a lot more than just putting some words on paper--that's the easy part. Here, right at the beginning, is the most important point I can teach you:

BEFORE YOU WRITE ANYTHING,

THINK!

Who are you writing to? What is the main idea you want to get across? How do you feel about it? How can you lead up to it? Should you be serious, or is there room for humor? How many words will it take to get the job done? What words will communicate this idea most clearly?

Thinking leads to writing, and writing to more thinking. In fact, learning to write will also help teach you to think!

EAGER ROOKIE JOINS NEWSPAPER STAFF
MOST PROMISING IN MANY YEARS, EDITOR SAYS

Before going any further, you'll have to fill out a job application to work on the newspaper. There's nothing to it; just complete the blanks below and on the next page. You should know all the answers except perhaps your Social Security Number. Businesses that pay their employees must have that number for complicated reasons that have to do with taxes. Ask your parents about your Social Security Number, and if you don't have one, we can still put you to work--that's because we don't pay anything!

APPLICATION FOR EMPLOYMENT

NAME (last, middle, first) _____

STREET ADDRESS _____

CITY, STATE, ZIP _____

SOCIAL SECURITY NUMBER _____ BIRTHDATE _____

FATHER'S NAME _____

OCCUPATION AND JOB TITLE _____

MOTHER'S NAME _____

OCCUPATION AND JOB TITLE _____

(continued on next page)

BEST FRIEND _____

NAME TWO ADULTS WHO ARE NOT RELATED TO YOU BUT KNOW YOU WELL:

_____

NAME OF YOUR LOCAL NEWSPAPER _____ _____

LIST THREE NEWSPAPER FEATURES THAT YOU WOULD MOST LIKE TO WRITE (see "Tour of the Newspaper" on p. 3):

_____

_____

_____

LIST FOUR PLACES THAT YOU ENJOY VISITING:

_____

_____

_____

_____

LIST TWO PEOPLE YOU KNOW WHO HAVE DONE SOMETHING INTERESTING LATELY:

_____

_____

LIST THREE OBJECTS THAT YOU WOULD LIKE TO RECEIVE AS COMPENSATION (that is, pay) FOR YOUR WORK:

_____

_____

_____

LIST ONE IDEA THAT YOU ENJOY THINKING ABOUT:

_____

PLEASE MARK ANY OF THE FOLLOWING CONDITIONS THAT AFFECT YOU:

Allergies:

____ Writers' Cramp   ____ Pencils
____ Nosittus Toolongus   ____ Paper
____ Wiggles   ____ Ink
                          ____ Thinking

IMAGINATION STRETCHERS

       We like employees who enjoy their work, even though that work can be demanding. That's why we encourage our writers to use their imaginations on assignments done "just for fun." Speaking of imagination, do you have one? Give yourself the following test to find out.

       Close your eyes. Can you picture what your grandmother looks like? A carousel? The local park? The outside of your house or apartment building? A zebra? An oak tree? If you answered "yes" to any of these questions, congratulations! You passed the imagination test and are qualified to try any of the imagination stretchers.

Now, suppose someone were applying for the position of your best friend, or your ideal little brother or big sister. What would you want to know about him or her? What would the application for a human cannonball or a rubber-chicken inspector look like?

In your notebook, write at least two application forms: one for an unusual job, and one for the position of friend or relative. Do you think it's a good thing that we don't have to "apply" to be someone's friend?

PART I:

NOUNS, VERBS AND BASIC SENTENCES

About 250 years ago, an Irish writer named Jonathan Swift wrote a story about the "Academy of Lagado," a made-up place where scientists conducted curious experiments and taught some strange ideas. Among the learned experts at this school were a group of linguists (people who study language) who had decided that words were not necessary. Words, they believed, were not real things. To communicate, they carried sacks of "real things" on their backs at all times, and had "conversations" by showing these objects to each other.

I'm glad this idea never caught on in our world!

Remember what our editor said on page 2? Because of language, *we can use words as symbols for real things.* One hundred objects on your back could get very heavy, but 100, or even 1000 words in your mind weigh nothing at all! From the time you learned to talk, you have used hundreds of words every day without even thinking about them.

Part of learning to write, however, means learning to think about words and how they work together in sentences. That's what the first two sections of this book are all about. We'll start with *nouns* and *verbs*, the two most important word groups a writer must know.

NOUNS ARE KEY TO LANGUAGE, EXPERTS AGREE

Take a moment to look back at your application on pages 4 and 5. You'll see that almost all the answers you wrote were **nouns**--people, places, things, and ideas. Many of your answers were **proper** nouns, or names of *particular* persons and places (such as Nike, Michigan, George Washington, and Binky). **Common** nouns are words that can apply to anything of a particular kind (such as shoes, state, president, and teddy bear).

Proper nouns are easy to recognize because they *always* begin with a capital letter. In the list below, write the common noun that shows what kind of object the proper noun is. The first two are done for you as an example. When you are finished, write today's date on the line below that reads, "I COMPLETED THIS LIST ON _____."

1. Schwinn _bicycle_

2. Burger King _restaurant_

3. Michigan _____

4. Houston _____

5. Bible _____

6. Wal-Mart _____

7. Christmas _____

8. Dr. Smith _____

9. Canada _____

I COMPLETED THIS LIST ON _____.

Sometimes nouns are difficult to recognize. Remember the editor's advice:

If a word can be used in a sentence with "a," "an," or "the" in front of it, that word is a noun.

Those three little words are called **articles**, but we think of them as "noun markers," because they are *only* used with nouns.

LIST MANIA STRIKES NEWSPAPER STAFF

Do you know anyone who makes lists? List-makers are usually people who have a lot to do and want to remember it all.

Another purpose for a list is to help us sort out what's important to us or understand what we are like. You made several short lists on your job application-- lists of persons, places and things. Turn back a couple of pages and look at your answers again. How many nouns do you think you listed? Count them and put the number here _____.

Every word in the following lists should be a noun. You may have a little trouble thinking of enough people, places, things and ideas to fill all the blank lines, especially in lists F and H. If you need help, ask a parent or family member for ideas, but don't just give up. Keep thinking until you complete all the blanks.

List A: Two of my favorite foods from each of the four food groups

Meat: Dairy:

_____   _____

_____   _____

Grains and cereals: Fruits and vegetables:

_____   _____

_____   _____

List B: Six sounds I enjoy hearing (such as musical instruments, particular voices, etc.)

_____   _____

_____   _____

_____   _____

List C: My five favorite places to go

_____   _____

_____   _____

_____

List D: Six things I don't like to see people throw away

_____   _____

_____   _____

_____   _____

List E: The perfect birthday present for each of three people in my family.

_____   _____

_____   _____

List F: Four qualities* I like in a best friend

_____   _____

_____   _____

(continued on the next page)

List G: Seven things I like to read about

_____   _____

_____   _____

_____   _____

_____

List H: Five qualities* I love about God

_____   _____

_____   _____

_____

*A *quality* is any feature of a thing (or person) that helps make it what it is. Qualities of people could be selfishness, intelligence, kindness, temper, generosity, humor, etc.

I COMPLETED THESE LISTS ON _____.

IMAGINATION STRETCHERS

Lists can tell you a lot about a person. On separate pages in your notebook, write three or four suggestions for lists and give each one to someone in your family to fill out. You may use the ideas above or any of your own. Here a few more: four places I like to see people go, five animals I would like to be (for a day), my four favorite trees, my seven favorite healthy snacks, three facial expressions I don't like.

I COMPLETED THIS ACTIVITY ON _____.

SPECIFIC NOUNS PREFERRED BY READERS, 3 to 1

Nouns can help you say exactly what you mean if you use them carefully. Our language contains general nouns (which could refer to several things) and more specific nouns (which refer only to a few things) "Furniture" can mean several types of objects, and so can "chair." But "armchair" is a particular *kind* of furniture. Most of us can picture an armchair immediately as something fairly large and stuffed--a great place to curl up with a book.

Notice how nouns become more specific in these examples, like a picture coming into focus:

instrument ⟶ drum ⟶ timpani

girl ⟶ dancer ⟶ ballerina

The following two exercises will help you see the difference between general and specific nouns. Suggested answers may be found on p. A in the back.

A. Look at the pictures below and try to think of three nouns for each, ranging from the most general to the most specific. Suggested answers are on page A. The first one is done for you as an example:

1.

picture
painting
portrait

2.

_____
_____
_____

3.

_____
_____
_____

4.

_____
_____
_____

5.

_____
_____
_____

6.

_____
_____
_____

B. Specific nouns can help you say what you want to say in fewer words. Instead of writing "a flower with a yellow center and white petals," the word "daisy" says it all. "A frosty orange-flavored drink" are five words to say "orange icee" (or "slurpee," depending on what part of the country you live in). Write one noun that will state, all by itself, what the following groups of words are trying to say. Check your answers on page A.

1. An automobile with a top that folds
   down.   It's a _____.

2. Curtains that hang from near the
   ceiling all the way to the floor   They're _____.

3. An evergreen tree with long "needles"
   instead of leaves.   It's a _____.

I COMPLETED THESE EXERCISES ON _____.

CLASSIFIED ADS SPEED SALES

Classified ads are "classified," or grouped, according to the product or service that is offered for sale. The Classified Ad sections take up about one-sixth of an entire paper. If you have something to sell, a classified ad is an effective way to get the word out to people who may want to buy. Of course, you have to pay for the ad, and most newspapers charge by the word. Therefore, every word counts! Your nouns must be clear and specific, and you should list only those features which will make the item more attractive to readers.

Which of these ads would be most likely to sell the item?

Nice car, runs good. Call 555-1122, ask for Jon.

1988 red car, small. Good motor with 150,000 miles. Call Jon at 555-1122.

1988 Mustang convertible. Like-new motor, only 150,000 miles. 555-1122; ask for Jon.

The third ad is more likely to attract buyers, just because all the words in it are carefully chosen. Think about that as you write your own classified ads.

Find three objects in your room to "sell" through a classified ad. Without stretching the truth, try to make these objects sound as attractive as you can, telling the size, color, use, or anything else that might help readers picture them. (Read some ads in one of your newspapers if you need more examples of how they are written.)

Your budget is limited--you may use no more than twenty words! You may or may not mention the price, but be sure to include your telephone number (which counts as one word).

FOR SALE: _____

_____

FOR SALE: _____

_____

FOR SALE: _____

_____

I COMPLETED THIS ASSIGNMENT ON _____.

IMAGINATION STRETCHERS: In your notebook, write three "For Sale" ads of thirty words or less offering unusual items. Here are a few suggestions: the space shuttle, a puppet theater, the British royal crown, your brother or sister, your brain, a brilliant idea.

I COMPLETED THIS ASSIGNMENT ON _____.

POETRY PLEASES PUBLIC

Now we'll try something a little different. Our "Poetry Corner" is one of the most popular features of the newspaper, and we often keep poems on hand to fill up space when necessary. If you don't have any spare poems we could use, let's try writing some **formal** poetry (written according to a set of rules, or a "form"). The form we will use is called cinquain (pronounced SING-kane, meaning "five").

By the way, don't be scared off by the word "poetry." A poem is just an expression of feelings or a word picture. The trick in writing poetry is to use just enough words to express your thoughts--no more, no less.

Follow these directions and you'll have a "cinquain-type" poem:

Example:

1. Write the name of a person close to you.   Alice

2 Write the name again, with one word that   Busy Alice
tells what this person is like.

3. Mention a part of this person's face or   Flying hands that never stop
body with two or three descriptive words.

4. Tell what that part is doing.   Setting shiny forks and knives
                                                        around the table

5. Reveal this person's relationship to you.   My grandma.

Now it's your turn. Follow the directions for each line:

1. _____

2. _____

3. _____

4. _____

5. _____

I COMPLETED THIS POEM ON_____.

Good try! Let's do a different one. This time, we'll be more strict about the words you can use. Each line will have to contain a certain number of syllables. A **syllable** is a single sound within a word. You may look up any word in a dictionary and see how it is divided into syllables.

Let's listen for some syllables first. With your pencil, tap out the sounds in each line of the following poem:

Mouse	1. (Name of animal --1 syllable)
Fright/ened mouse	2. (Animal with 1-2 descriptive words--3 syllables)
Whis/kers qui/ver,paws	(Words to show what the animal does):
	3. 5 syllables on line 3
Pat/ter on the hard wood floor	4. 7 syllables on line 4
Mouse.	5. (Repeat of line 1)

Now write a poem about a "one-syllable" animal (cow, pig, horse, cat, etc.) following the directions on the example you just tapped out.

1. _____

2. _____

3. _____

4. _____

5. _____

I COMPLETED THIS POEM ON _____.

Here's another one--and we won't count syllables this time. Look out the window: what do you see? Write one noun on the first line:

Example:

Clouds	1. (Noun)
Fluffy, floating	2. (2 words to describe it)
High in the autumn sky	3. (4-6 words to tell where it is)
Wanting to come down and talk to us	4. (6-8 words to tell what it's thinking—if it could think!)
Lonely drifters	5. (one noun and one descriptive word that pictures the object as a person)

1. _____

2. _____

3. _____

4. _____

5. _____

I COMPLETED THIS POEM ON _____.

As we said, formal poetry is written according to a set of rules. All the poems you wrote and all three examples are different, and yet they are alike in three ways. What are they? Think about it, then write on the lines below your <u>Three Rules For Writing A Formal Poem</u>:

1. _____

_____

2. _____

_____

3. _____

_____

Look at the box on page A. If the rules in the box are like yours, you won't have to change anything. If the book says something very different from what you wrote, change your rules (or the parts that are not correct) to agree with the book's.

I COMPLETED THIS ACTIVITY ON _____.

As long as you follow the basic guidelines, you can write a poem about anything. Here's one more example:

`Fear`	(Name a strong feeling you have experienced.)
`Crawly fear`	(Repeat, with one descriptive word.)
`Sweaty hands shake in my lap`	(Describe a part of your body that reflects this feeling, in 4-6 words.)
`"The Dentist is ready to see you now."`	(Write the statement said by someone that makes you feel this way--6-8 words, inside quotation marks.)
`Oh, no!`	(Write 1-2 words that express your feeling in another way.)

IMAGINATION STRETCHER

Draw a straight line down the middle of a page in your notebook. Choose a noun as the subject for a formal poem. Write the noun on the top left side of the paper, and then decide what each line will contain. Write directions for your poem on the right side of the paper (ask a parent if you need help in thinking of directions) Then finish your poem on the left.

I COMPLETED THIS POEM ON _____.

Now, write complete and clear directions (with an example) for a poem similar to the one on the top of page 15. It can be about anything, and you can make up the rules about what goes on each line. Then ask a friend or family member to write the poem!

_____ **COMPLETED THIS POEM ON _____.**

WRITERS AGREE: VERBS VITAL

Remember: *nouns are the key to any language.* But if nouns were the only words we knew, we would not be much better off than those "experts" at Lagoda who communicated only with objects. Nouns have to *do* something. That's where **verbs** come in. Let's review the three types of verbs: *action, linking* and *helping*.

Action verbs tell what something or someone does:

`Night `<u>`fell`</u>`.      The batter `<u>`walked`</u>`.      Amanda `<u>`shouted`</u>`.`

Helping verbs go along with action verbs to show a change in time or meaning:

`Night `<u>`had`</u>` fallen.     The batter `<u>`can`</u>` walk.     Amanda `<u>`is`</u>` shouting.`

Linking verbs connect (or "link") a noun or pronoun with another word that describes it:

`The night `<u>`was`</u>` cold.     The batter `<u>`seems`</u>` happy.     Amanda `<u>`is`</u>` excited.`

Usually, a word is an action verb if it makes sense with "-ing" on the end of it. One exception is "being," which is a linking verb. As our sports editor pointed out, our language contains lots of interesting action verbs, and it's fun to use them.

This might be a good time to talk about another book that would be a great help to you in your writing career.

THESAURUS

Suppose you lived next door to a "Word Shop," stocked with every word you would ever want to use. If you walked into this shop and said, "I'm looking for another word for *walk*," the helpful salesperson could pull out the "walk" drawer and show you: **step, tread, stroll, pace, hike,** and **ambulate.**

If one of these words was just what you wanted, you could make your purchase and happily ambulate home. Or, if none of them would suit, you could ask to see more: in the "pace" drawer you would find **stride** and **gait.** If neither of *these* would do, you could continue trying on words, like shoes, until you found exactly the right one or until the helpful salesperson ran out of patience.

It may surprise you to know that a "word shop" does exist. It comes between two covers, and you can use it like a dictionary. It's called a **thesaurus**. This is a book containing synonyms (words with similar meaning) for just about any word you would want to use. No writer can get along without one.

Use your thesaurus to complete these exercises.

A. Look up the following words in your thesaurus and write at least four synonyms for these nine actions:

1. walk _____

_____

2. sit _____

_____

3. run _____

_____

4. shout _____

_____

5. talk _____

_____

6. stand _____

_____

7. fly _____

_____

8. hit _____

_____

9. laugh _____

_____

I COMPLETED THIS EXERCISE ON _____.

B. Now we'll go on a word "hunt." You will be "tracking down" the *perfect* verb to express how these animals move. You may be able to find it in the lists you made in the previous exercise, but for some of the words you'll have to look in your thesaurus. Start by looking up the word "move." Then choose the verb that seems closest to the kind of movement made by that animal, and look up *that* word. Keep looking up words until you find just the right one.

1. The cat _____.   5. The cheetah _____.

2. The robin _____.   6. The calf _____.

3. The bear _____.   7. The pony _____.

4. The snake _____.   8. The octopus _____.

I COMPLETED THIS EXERCISE ON _____.

VERBS WANTED

It's time to write more classified ads. Classifieds are used not only for selling, but also for finding workers to do a job. In the "help wanted" ads below, underline all the verbs you find. You may check your answers on page A.

Help Wanted: Pastry chef. Baking, decorating and sweeping required. Hourly wage. Apply in person at La Petite Maison; ask for Jose.

Help Wanted: Companion for elderly millionaire. Job involves dusting, vacuuming, cooking and reading aloud. Salary includes excellent investment tips.

Think of two jobs you do at home and write ads for someone to take your place. In each one, after HELP WANTED, write the name of the occupation, then list the actions involved in doing this job. That way, the reader will know whether he or she can handle it. Next, inform the job-seeker where to go or what number to call, and be sure to write what compensation (pay) the employment offers.

HELP WANTED:_____

_____

_____

_____

HELP WANTED:_____

_____

_____

_____

I COMPLETED THIS ASSIGNMENT ON _____.

Now push your imagination a bit further and write classified ads for these jobs. Be sure to include at least three verbs in each one to make it clear what the job is like. Complete the ads with information about pay and the person to contact. Write ads for the occupations below, then make up two jobs of your own:

1. HELP WANTED (mother):_____

_____

_____

_____

(continued on next page)

2. HELP WANTED (President of the U.S.):_____

_____

_____

_____

3. HELP WANTED (missionary):_____

_____

_____

_____

4. HELP WANTED (astronaut):_____

_____

_____

_____

5. HELP WANTED (you choose): _____

_____

_____

_____

6. HELP WANTED (you choose): _____

_____

_____

_____

I COMPLETED THIS ASSIGNMENT ON _____.

VIVID VERBS VAPORIZE VAPID VERBS
(WHAT IN THE WORLD DOES "VAPID" MEAN? ASKS EDITOR)

Think of a sports activity you enjoy. It can be anything from organized soccer to jumping rope.

Write a description of that activity based on verbs. Start each line with a STRONG (or "vivid") action verb ending in "-ing." Your Thesaurus can be a great help with this. For example: Before you write "hitting the ball" or "running down the field," look up the verb *hit* or *run* and look at the synonyms listed. You may find one you like better. Once you have your "-ing" verb, add words to complete the thought. On the last line, write the name of the game. Your sports description will look like a poem, and maybe it is!

Example: Whacking the bouncy yellow ball,
Sprinting across the court just in time,
Skidding to a stop and
Swooshing my racket through the air--thunk!
That's tennis.

Write a sports description, five lines, like the example above.

_____

_____

_____

_____

_____

I COMPLETED THIS ASSIGNMENT ON _____.

Think of a sport or game you've never played, but wish you could. Can you imagine what it might be like? Write another description like the one above, based on what you can imagine. (Our sports editor probably won't know the difference between the game you played and the one you didn't!)

_____

_____

_____

_____

_____

I COMPLETED THIS ASSIGNMENT ON _____.

IMAGINATION STRETCHER

What do you suppose your shoes would tell you if they could talk? In your notebook, describe a typical morning from the point of view of your shoes (once they are on your feet). Tell what they do in one morning, using some of the verbs from the thesaurus exercise on page 19.

I COMPLETED THIS ASSIGNMENT ON _____.

LINKING VERBS SIMPLIFY COMPLEX TASK

You may have noticed that we haven't said much about linking verbs. That's because you already know what they are and use them every day without even thinking about it. But here's a situation where it's useful to think about linking verbs--when writing definitions. Has this ever happened to you:

TEACHER: Define "polyglot."

YOU: "Polyglot." That's . . . uh . . . that's where you . . . No, I mean it's when . . . uh . . . .

There must be a better way! You'll find it much easier to write or say a definition by using a linking verb to help organize your thoughts. We'll have much more to say about organizing thoughts later, but defining words in a single sentence is a good way to start.

Here's how to write the definition for a *noun*. After the word itself--the target word--write a linking verb: usually *is* or *are*. Next, write a noun that names the general group or category that this word falls into. Follow this with another type of "linking" word: *who* for people, *which* for objects, and *that* for animals, people, or objects. Finally, explain how the target word is different from others in the general group. Does it sound hard? Study the example in the chart below, noticing how the parts of the definition work together. Then try writing your own definitions of the target words. Ask a parent or look up the word in a dictionary if you don't know what it means. We've left two lines blank for you to define your own target words.

TARGET WORD	LINKING VERB	GENERAL GROUP	(that, which, who)	WHAT MAKES TARGET WORD SPECIAL
1. (a) journalist	is	a writer	who	works for a newspaper or magazine
2. (a newspaper) feature				
3. (a) masthead				
4.				
5.				

I COMPLETED THIS ASSIGNMENT ON _____.

The formula for defining verbs is a little different. We'll use a little word that's often found in front of an action verb: the word "to."

To write a verb definition, start with a target verb and the word "to." Next, write "is the act of," since action verbs show action. Follow this with the general type of action this verb shows, and end with a description of what makes it special. With verbs, this usually means explaining how, when, where or by what the action is done.

Again, study how the description is written in the examples below, then write your own descriptions of the target words.

TARGET WORD	"is the act of"	GENERAL ACTION	how, when, where or by what?
1. to edit	is the act of	correcting and pre-paring a written work	for publication
2. to revise			
3. to investigate			
4.			
5.			

I COMPLETED THIS ASSIGNMENT ON _____.

Now you've learned the two most important parts of any language: nouns and verbs. Nouns are the naming words, and verbs are the action words. But it's not enough to know what these are; a writer must also learn how they are put together in sentences. That's what our editor will be talking about next.

SENTENCES MAKE SENSE

It may be a little difficult to understand **subjects** and **predicates**, so let's try an experiment. Look around you. In the box below, write four sentences about things you see, observing these two guidelines:

1. Do not start a sentence with the word "there," as in, "There is" or "There are."
2. Use action verbs rather than linking verbs in at least three of the sentences. Instead of "The clock *is* on the mantel," for example, write, "The clock *ticks* on the mantel."

If someone is in the room with you, be sure to tell what he or she is doing. Write the *subject* of each sentence in the boxes on the left, and the *predicate* in the boxes on the right.

	Subject	Predicate
1.	My sister	is washing the dishes.
2.		
3.		
4.		
5.		

Now read your sentences out loud, but mix them up. That is, read subject #1 of the example with predicate #2 in your sentence, subject #2 with predicate #3, and so on. How does it sound? Chances are your sentences won't make any logical sense--but, if you divided them correctly, they will *sound* like proper sentences.

I COMPLETED THIS ASSIGNMENT ON _____.

That's the way our language works: we put words in a certain order that all English speakers understand. The subject of the sentence comes before the verb. If this seems natural to you, you may be surprised to know that in many languages, the order of the words in a sentence does not matter. The subject can go anywhere! But in English, each part of a sentence has its place. That's why it's very important to understand how sentences are put together if you want to write well.

SENTENCE FORMS SURPRISINGLY SIMPLE

You only need to know two basic sentence forms:

(1) subject// verb   (2) subject//verb/object

subject // predicate   subject // predicate

The **subject** is always a noun, or a word that takes the place of a noun (such as a pronoun).

The **verb** is always the most important part of the predicate, and may even be a predicate all by itself.

Often a verb takes an object. An **object** shows what (or who) the action is done to, as in:

```
slam the door   read the speech     eat a cookie     hug you
```

As you can see, the object in all these examples is a noun or a pronoun. Many pronouns, in fact, do something very interesting when they become objects. Suppose you said to your mother "I'll hug you if you hug I." She would probably reply, "I'll be glad to, but you must say, 'if you hug *me*.'" You can hear right away that "hug I" is not correct. When you were learning to speak, you never heard anyone say it that way. Now you know the reason why: *Certain pronouns have both a subject form **and** an object form.*

Below is a list of some of these pronouns. Write a short subject/verb/object sentence using each form, first as the subject, then as an object.

EXAMPLE:

I, me   *I picked a rose.   My friend likes me.*

1. She, her _____

2. He, him _____

3. We, us _____

I COMPLETED THIS EXERCISE ON _____.

With some slight variations, all sentences are built on one of the two basic models: **subject/verb** or **subject/verb/object**. That's why nouns and verbs are so important--they are the words that make up the "heart" of every sentence.

Of course, communicating only with nouns and verbs would limit what we could say. Let's try an experiment. Write five related sentences using only the two basic sentence models. That is, you may use nouns and verbs, plus the noun markers "the," "a," and "an." Pronouns like "he," "it," and "her" are permitted, and helping verbs ("had seen", "is going", for example), but *nothing* else. You'll find it may take some thought! You should come up with something like this example:

```
     My foot itched.  Mom helped me.  She got a
can.  She sprinkled powder.  The powder stopped
the itch.  I could run.
```

Now you try it:

(continued on next page)

_____

_____

_____

I COMPLETED THIS EXERCISE ON _____.

If you had to read stuff like this all the time, you would soon lose interest in reading. Sentences are, of course, much more complicated than the simple structure you used above, and it's a good thing, too. But *every* sentence is built around a basic subject/verb combination.

COMPOUNDING MAKES READERS SEE DOUBLE

Let's discuss a slightly different form of the subject/verb model. It's possible for a sentence to have a double subject, a double verb, or a double object; even to "double" itself! This is called **compounding**. To discover a compound anything, watch for these three little words: *and, but, or*. Sometimes the pairs *either...or* or *neither...nor* are used in compound sentences. These words are called **conjunctions**. Notice how conjunctions are used in these examples:

<u>Sarah and Jolene</u> left an hour ago.   (compound subject)
Hank <u>swept and washed</u> the sidewalk.   (compound verb)
Please call <u>Scott or his mother</u>.   (compound object)
Ning Mei <u>found her purse but lost her socks</u>.   (compound predicate)
<u>I'll address the cards and Kelly will mail them</u>.   (compound sentence)

In the space beside each sentence below, write whether the underlined portion is a compound *subject, verb, object, predicate*, or *sentence*. Answers on page A.

1. I know <u>Terri and her sister</u>.   _____

2. Jack will <u>either go with us or stay home</u>.   _____

3. <u>Ali and Pat</u> started the race together.   _____

4. Cameron <u>slipped but did not fall</u>.   _____

5. <u>Not Missy but Frieda</u> will speak first.   _____

6. Mrs. Alvarez made <u>cookies and lemonade</u>.   _____

I COMPLETED THIS EXERCISE ON _____.

INVESTIGATIVE REPORTERS DISCOVER FOUR SENTENCE TYPES

In the next few pages we'll learn about the four **sentence types**. Don't confuse **types** with **models**. The models that we've learned show how sentences are arranged, but the types show four different *purposes* a sentence can have.

DECLARATIVE SENTENCES STATE FACTS

All the sentences we've been talking about so far belong to a category called **declarative**. Declarative sentences simply state (or "declare") a fact or idea, and they always follow those basic models of **subject/verb** or **subject/verb/object**. Most sentences that you read and write fall into this class. In fact, all the sentences in this paragraph are declarative.

The other three sentence types don't exactly follow the two models you've learned so well. Let's see how they work.

INTERROGATIVE SENTENCES ASK QUESTIONS

They are easy to recognize because of the question mark (?) at the end, but you probably never noticed something very peculiar about the structure: in most interrogative sentences, the subject nouns and the verbs are reversed! Observe how a simple declarative sentence can be turned into a question:

```
You are happy.              George Washington was President.
Are you happy?             Was George Washington President?
```

Write your own subject/verb declarative sentence and turn it into a question by reversing the subject and verb:

_____

_____

Besides reversing the verb, we often make use of the helping verbs "do," "did," "does," and "will" to ask questions:

```
Terry played the violin.    Dr. Smith will speak now.
Did Terry play the violin?  Will Dr. Smith speak now?
```

Write two "helping verb" examples here:

_____

_____

We also use the question words **who, what, when, where, why,** and **how** to ask questions (but these words are *not* verbs).

<u>Where</u> are my keys?
<u>When</u> does the party start?
<u>How</u> did you get chocolate all over your face?

On the lines below, write three interrogative sentences beginning with one of the six question words (**who**, **what**, **when**, **where**, **why** and **how**):

_____

_____

_____

I COMPLETED THESE THREE EXERCISES ON _____.

IMPERATIVE SENTENCES GIVE ORDERS OR DIRECTIONS

Parents and teachers use quite a lot of **imperative** sentences, like these:

Pick up your pencils.   Follow the red line.

The addition of "please" to an imperative sentence makes it a polite request. No doubt you hear lots of imperative sentences every day, but you probably never noticed a very suspicious fact about them:

The Mystery of the Disappearing SUBJECT

Here's what we mean. Below are three short sentences, explaining how to brush your teeth:

Put about 1/4 inch of toothpaste on the brush.
Run a little water from the faucet over the brush.
Rub your teeth and gums with the brush bristles, using
    a circular motion.

Now, try to find the subject in each of the sentences.

You'll find that all three sentences, contrary to our sentence models, don't seem to have a subject. They don't appear to obey the subject/verb model, so how can they make sense?

Suppose we were sitting together in a room and you read your directions to me. Whom are you instructing? Me, that's whom! Except that I would be "you" to you--get it? All imperative sentences are addressed to someone known as "you"-- they tell "you" to do something or instruct "you" in how to do it.

Therefore "you" is the subject of most imperative sentences, even though the word does not actually appear!

On the lines below, write three imperative sentences telling how to put on a coat:

_____

_____

_____

I COMPLETED THIS EXERCISE ON _____.

If several people are together and we only want to talk to one of them, we can make that clear by naming him or her. In this case, the person named is the subject of the command.

`Jack, pick up your pencils.`   `Girls, follow the red line.`

EXCLAMATORY SENTENCES EXPRESS STRONG FEELING

Strong feeling may be added to any sentence just by placing an exclamation mark at the end (!). Other exclamatory "sentences," however, can break all the rules of sentence form (and get away with it) because they are used to show excitement, admiration, pain, or any other strong emotion. The word "What" is often used for this purpose.

`What a catch!`   `What a mess!`   `What nerve!`

Imperative sentences are often exclamatory sentences also:

`Look at him go!`   `Watch out for that car!`   `Bless my soul!`

Often, an exclamatory "sentence" is no more than one word long. These are sometimes called **exclamations**, because they are not considered real sentences.

`Wow!`   `Awesome!`   `Ouch!`   `Hey!`

These are just a few examples of exclamatory sentences! Any declarative sentence can be exclamatory, too! All you have to do is put an exclamation mark at the end! But the thing to remember is, don't overdo it!

On the lines below, write three exclamatory sentences about your most interesting relative:

_____

_____

_____

_____

I COMPLETED THIS EXERCISE ON _____.

CAPTION WRITING OFFERS EXCELLENT PRACTICE

Almost every picture in a newspaper includes a **caption**: a line or two that explains briefly what the picture is about. When the picture is part of a newspaper story, the caption may be as short as one word. But sometimes the picture stands alone, without an article to go with it. In that case, the caption serves as a "ministory," and may be several sentences long.

The pictures below need captions to explain their meaning to readers. Since no one wrote an article to go along with these, you will write a four-sentence caption. For each picture, write two declarative sentences, one interrogative sentence, and one exclamation. You do not have to write them in any particular order.

EXAMPLE:

Serena Oliver was awarded first prize for her special cauliflower pickles at the County Fair on Wednesday. Dexter Spikes presided over the final judging. Way to go, Serena! Could the judge's face be called a pickle puss?

_____

_____

_____

_____

_____

_____

_____

_____

_____

_____

_____

_____

_____

_____

_____

_____

_____

YOU ARE INVITED

We're going to take a break from newspaper writing in order to get some extra practice on sentences. The use of imperative sentences is especially common in instruction books, like this one. A more welcome use, perhaps, is in invitations. Sentences like, "Come to a party," are imperative, but much nicer to hear than sentences like, "Go clean up your room." If you could host the ideal party, what would you do? Write an invitation following these guidelines:

1. An imperative sentence explaining what kind of party it will be.
2. A declarative sentence telling when and where the party will be.
3. An imperative sentence telling what to wear, bring, or be prepared for.
4. A declarative sentence explaining what you expect to do at the party.

---

1. *Please come to* _____

_____

2. *The party will begin* _____

at _____

3. *Be sure to* _____

_____

4. *We will* _____

_____

I COMPLETED THIS ASSIGNMENT ON _____.

Suppose every event around your house required an invitation. Using the model above, write another invitation to one of the following:

1. Giving the baby a bath
2. Changing a flat tire
3. Dinner
4. A shopping trip
5. Washing windows
6. (Do you have any ideas?)

_____

_____

_____

_____

_____

_____

I COMPLETED THIS ASSIGNMENT ON _____.

IMAGINATION STRETCHERS

In your notebook, write an invitation for a very unusual event. Here are some suggestions:

A moon walk--on the moon
A trying-on-hats party at an exclusive store
A funeral for a dead pair of sneakers
A burn-your-old-spelling-tests party
Bon voyage for a trip to Antarctica

If you like, copy your invitation on stationery or card stock and decorate it with stickers or drawings. Use your imagination!

I COMPLETED THIS ASSIGNMENT ON _____.

LETTER-WRITING SURGES, SAYS POSTMASTER

If letters make words, do words make letters? Of course--and one of the most important ways you'll ever use your sentence-writing skills is in the letters you send to family and friends throughout your life. Letters do take longer than a phone call, but they *last* longer, too. When you hang up the phone, your listener has already forgotten half of what you said. But letters can be kept as long as the reader chooses to keep them. If you have something really special to say, the rule is: *put it in a letter*.

One type of letter you should already have experience writing is the Thank-You note.

When you tear the paper off a Christmas package and find just the gift you wanted inside, it's all right to yell, "Thank you, Grandma!" across the room at her. But it's so much better to write her a personal note, and I wouldn't be surprised if she keeps it forever.

It isn't hard. If you've had a birthday or received some gifts lately, list them below. In the first space, write the giver's name. In the second, write the name of the gift--and be specific! Don't just write "game," write "Monopoly" or "Bingo" game. In the third space, write how you plan to use it or one particular thing you like about it. The first line is filled in as an example:

GIVER	GIFT	HOW I'LL USE IT/WHAT I LIKE ABOUT IT
1. Aunt Louise	Jenga blocks	exciting when blocks fall down
2.		
3.		
4.		
5.		

I COMPLETED THIS LIST ON _____.

Once you have your list, it's easy to write the notes. Just use your list as a rough outline of what you want to say, and put the thoughts in sentence form. To make your letter more interesting, include one exclamatory or interrogative sentence.

EXAMPLE:

Dear Aunt Louise,

    Thank you for the Jenga Blocks. Carl, David and I have already played many games. I think it's really exciting when we get near the end and everybody is so afraid that their block is the one that will make the whole tower fall down! Thank you for remembering my birthday.

                       Love, Jenny

Write your notes on attractive cards or stationery, or design your own cards with stickers, stamps and colored paper. (If it hasn't been too long since you received your gifts why not go ahead and mail these cards?)

        I COMPLETED THIS ASSIGNMENT ON _____.

IMAGINATION STRETCHER:

Write a note to someone thanking him or her for something that can't be wrapped up in a box. This could be a kind action, a thoughtful word, or something about him or her that you appreciate. After you've written the note, be sure to deliver it!

        I COMPLETED THIS ASSIGNMENT ON _____.

HEADLINES MAKE HEADLINES

Now we're back in the newspaper office.

A **headline** serves as the title of a newspaper story or feature. Its main purpose is to express the main point in a few words. You may have heard grown-ups mention that they don't read all of the paper--they "skim the headlines," meaning that they read only those words in the large dark type. If they come across a headline that interests them, they may wish to read the entire article. Every editor knows that no one reader will be interested in everything in the newspaper. The headline is a "flag" to signal what's in a story.

What's the difference between a **title** and a headline? The main difference has to do with purpose. Titles are supposed to attract interest and provide a memorable "handle" for a book, story, song, play, etc. Headlines should attract interest, but their main purpose, as we've seen, is to express the main point of a story.

Another important difference is in the structure. Very few titles are complete sentences. But almost all headlines are complete sentences, each with a subject and a verb. The words "the," "an," and "a" are dropped, and linking verbs like "is" and "was" are often dropped also. Notice the differences in these two examples:

Titles:	Headlines:
The Princess and the Pea	PRINCESS EXHAUSTED AFTER SLEEPLESS NIGHT
Little Jack Horner	BAD BOY MAKES GOOD (If he wasn't bad, why was he in the corner?)

Below are four recent headlines from our newspaper. On each headline, draw a vertical line between the subject and the predicate. Then underline the subject noun, and circle the verb. (Be careful--one of the headlines contains an **implied** verb--a linking verb that does not actually appear.) If the headline contains an object, underline that also. Check page A to see if you were correct.

1. MAYOR ORDERS INVESTIGATION

2. RECORD SNOWS FORCE SCHOOLS TO CLOSE

3. FAITHFUL DOG DRIVES OFF ATTACKER AND SAVES OWNER

4. SEVEN STUDENTS ON HONOR ROLL

Look up two headlines in your local paper and write them on the lines below. Then see if you can divide and mark them as you did in the headlines above.

1. _____

2. _____

I COMPLETED THIS ASSIGNMENT ON _____.

Writing headlines is not as easy as it looks. Space is usually limited, so there's no room for wasted words. Nouns and verbs, naturally, carry all the "weight" in a headline, so they must be carefully chosen. In a comical or lighthearted story a writer may have a little fun by choosing words that start with the same letter or sound (this is called **alliteration**-see headline on page 22 for an example). Rhyming words are fun, too (MICE LIKE RICE, RESEARCHERS DISCOVER), But harder to write in a way that makes sense.

Below is a list of newspaper stories that were turned in without headlines. Write two possible headlines for each one, then mark the one you like best. Use your Thesaurus to find interesting verbs.

EXAMPLE:

The church garden party was rained out--after all the guests had arrived.

Cloudburst Great For Garden, Not Garden Parties
Soggy Guests Seek Shelter In Sanctuary

1. Two bank robbers were caught with the cash because they locked themselves out of their getaway car.

_____

_____

2. An unusual piece of indian pottery was found in the vacant lot behind the grocery store.

_____

_____

3. A ten-year-old boy won the state spelling bee in spite of the fact that he is hearing-impaired.

_____

_____

4. A 63-year-old woman won the Gray Panther Pride cross-country marathon by 2.9 seconds.

_____

_____

(continued on next page)

5. A food fight at the County Fair disrupted the pie-judging.

_____

_____

6. Aliens were spotted buying frosty fruit-flavored drinks at a local 7-Eleven.

_____

_____

7. Television watching is limited in households where families play and pray together.

_____

_____

8. A baby was born to Samantha, the zoo's most popular attraction. Both mother and little one are doing well.

_____

_____

9. Three sets of identical twins live on the same street, and the neighbors are always getting them confused.

_____

_____

I COMPLETED THIS ASSIGNMENT ON _____.

PART TWO:

MODIFIERS AND MORE COMPLEX SENTENCES

A sentence is built on a subject and a verb. Everything else in the sentence is a **modifier**. Modifiers explain something about the subject, verb or object in the sentence.

It's as difficult to imagine language without modifiers as it is to imagine a world without color. How could you tell someone about your best friend if you had no words to say how tall he is, or how often she smiles, or how much he makes you laugh, or how easy she is to talk to? We use modifiers to express what someone or something is like.

In the next section, you will learn about the three major types of modifiers: *adjectives*, *adverbs*, and *prepositional phrases*. Let's see what our editor has to say about these.

MODIFIERS COMPLETE SENTENCES
LEARN TO RECOGNIZE THEM, WRITERS ADVISE

You've learned the basic form of a sentence. *Everything else* in the sentence is a modifier of some kind. In this section we will learn what the chief modifiers are.

ADJECTIVES SPOTTED BESIDE NOUNS

Adjectives are usually placed before the nouns they modify. But there is one exception: sometimes, adjectives follow a linking verb (see page 18 if you don't remember what a linking verb is).

When an adjective follows a linking verb, it is called a **complement**. This is because the adjective goes along with (or "complements") the subject.

But nouns can be complements, too! How can you tell if the word after a linking verb is a noun or an adjective? Compare the sentences below:

a. Mr. Jones is a <u>policeman</u>.   b. The girls are <u>students</u>.
    Mr. Jones is <u>brave</u>.   The girls are <u>lonely</u>.

In your mind, read the underlined word in each sentence *before* the subject: "Policeman Mr. Jones." "Brave Mr. Jones." Which combination sounds better?

If "brave Mr. Jones" sounds better, then "brave" must be an adjective. If "lonely girls" makes more sense than "students girls," then "lonely" is an adjective. If any word sounds correct and makes sense when you hear it in front of a simple noun, like "girl" or "man" . . . it's an adjective.

Circle the adjectives in each word group that will complete the sentence. Think carefully--some groups contain more than one adjective. Check your answers on page A.

1. The (is, grow, pretty, tapes) girl sighed.

2. The (lose, newspapers, red-headed, friendly) boy smiled.

3. Tony was (pleased, were, squirrel, upset).

4. The (books, handsome, around, bashful) gentlemen paused.

5. The students are (run, noisy, beside).

I COMPLETED THIS EXERCISE ON _____.

Every word in a sentence has a job to do. *The job of the adjective is to modify, or describe, a noun.*

That's easy to remember, isn't it? You can begin helping us with adjectives right away.

WRITERS IN SOCIAL WHIRL

The following two articles will be part of our society page, once you fill in all the blank spaces with a word that seems to fit. Ask a parent, older brother, or sister to help if you can't think of any suitable words. You should be able to think of all kinds of words, but they will share one thing in common: *all will be adjectives*. The spaces simply could not be filled with anything else!

LOCAL CELEBRITIES PULL FOR CHARITY

The third annual Hospital Auxiliary Tug-of-War and Mud Slide was a _____ success. Our city's finest took part, including Mayor O. B. Juste, Channel 4's _____ meteorologist Sunny McCloud, the suave and _____ attorney, Owen Sosume, and local author Tourna Paige. Shortly after noon at Central Park, captains Juste and Paige chose their teams, which then took their places on opposite sides of a _____ mud puddle created for this _____ occasion. To the _____ cheers of their fans, the two teams seesawed back and forth until Paige's _____ band gave a mighty tug and pulled our _____ mayor and his team into the _____ puddle. A _____ time was had by all, and the hospital auxiliary reports that the two _____ tug-of-war teams raised over $2000 to buy new play equipment for the children's ward.

DREW-SAWYER NUPTIALS

Ms. Nancy Drew and Mr. Thomas T. Sawyer were wed last Thursday in a _____ ceremony at First Community Church. The bride wore a _____, _____ gown with _____ sleeves and a _____ train. The church sanctuary, decorated by Wedding Belles, Inc., bloomed with a romantic and _____ blend of _____ roses, _____ doves, and festoons of _____ ribbon. The bride's attendants wore formal-length _____ dresses and carried bouquets of _____ daisies. The bride and groom repeated their vows in the _____ light of one hundred candles. To close the ceremony, all the guests were invited to rise and sing one _____ chorus of "_____."

(write the title of your favorite song here)

I COMPLETED THIS ASSIGNMENT ON _____.

ADVERBS ANSWER FOUR QUESTIONS

Adverbs are a bit harder to recognize than adjectives because they can be placed almost anywhere in a sentence. But they are modifiers, too. Adverbs modify verbs, as you might easily guess. But sometimes they modify adjectives and other adverbs!

The job of an adverb in the sentence is to tell *when, where, how,* or *how much.* Let's explore these words a little further.

If the adverb modifies a **verb**, it will tell *when, where* or *how* something happened. In the list of adverbs below, draw lines to match each word with the question that it answers.

yesterday	when?
there	
well	where?
often	
now	how?
badly	
very	how much?

At times, however, an adverb can modify an adjective, or even another adverb. When that happens, the adverb tells *how much*. Some examples are:

<u>pretty</u> scary (adverb modifies an adjective)
<u>very</u> loud (adverb modifies an adjective)
<u>fairly</u> often (adverb modifies another adverb)

One more interesting fact you should know about adverbs is that they can often be formed from adjectives by adding the letters "-ly."

beautiful becomes <u>beautifully</u>;

easy becomes <u>easily</u>;

Notice that the letter "y" at the end of **easy** is turned into an "i" before adding "ly."

cold becomes _____;

warm becomes _____;

quick becomes _____;

Remember that the "y" at the end of **shaky** must be changed to an "i" before adding the "ly" ending.

shaky becomes _____;

Can you think of some adjective-to-adverb transformations?

_____ becomes _____;

_____ becomes _____;

_____ becomes _____.

I COMPLETED THESE EXERCISES ON _____.

This "adding -ly" trick will not work for every adjective, and every word with "-ly" on the end is *not* an adverb. But it's interesting to see how words sometimes change *form* in order to show a change in *function*.

ROOKIE WRITERS REPORT: MODIFIERS ARE FUN!

Now that you understand adjectives and adverbs, we need some help with our "Fun Page." You've seen these--newspaper pages full of jokes, riddles and puzzles. This one is devoted to adjectives and adverbs. Please complete the page for us:

A. MYSTERY SACKS

In each of the sacks below is a "mystery" item. Can you guess what it is by the words used to describe it?

(Your instructions: decide what's in the bag--obviously something small enough to fit--and write four adjectives for each, describing how the item feels, sounds, or smells. See if other people can guess what it is from the adjectives you wrote.)

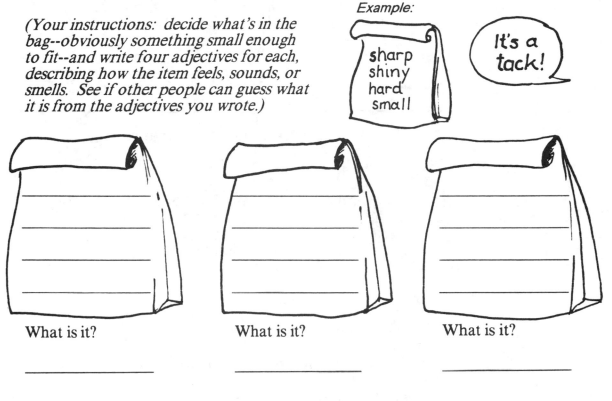

Example:

sharp
shiny
hard
small

It's a tack!

What is it?

_____

What is it?

_____

What is it?

_____

I COMPLETED THIS ASSIGNMENT ON _____.

B. WORD PORTRAITS

Did you know that pictures can be "painted" with words? In boxes within the frames on the next page, write the names of two people you know. Opposite each letter of the person's name, write an adjective beginning with that letter which describes the person.

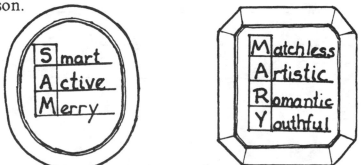

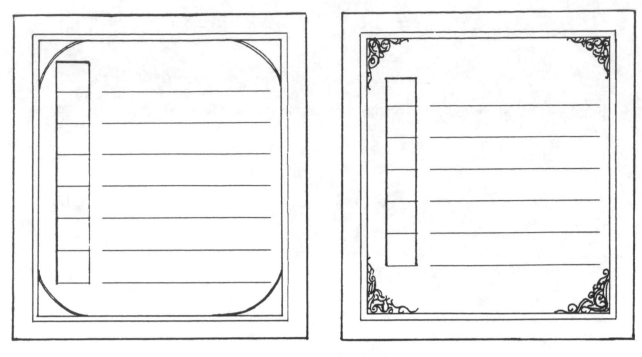

I COMPLETED THIS ASSIGNMENT ON _____.

C. "TOM SWIFTIES"

A character created by Edward Applegate, Tom Swift, was famous both for his brilliant inventions *and* for the way he said things. Tom used lots of adverbs--the kind that end in "ly"--that reflected the way he felt ("I'll never see her again," said Tom sorrowfully). A "Tom Swiftie" is a one-line joke that plays on the double meaning of an adverb. These two examples show how they work:

"I will be the first to try our new hair tonic," said Tom baldly.

"Did anyone catch the license number of that steam roller?" said Tom flatly.

To write a "Tom Swiftie," first think of an adverb (or adjective) that can have a double meaning. If you make a list of all the "ly" words you can think of, you'll probably find at least one. Here's a short list to get you started:

dully, smoothly, handily, friskily, sweetly, hotly, coldly, stoutly

Once you've found your adverb, think of something Tom could say that would point out the other meaning of the word. Write two "Tom Swifties" yourself, then challenge a friend or your teacher to think of one.

1. _____

_____

2. _____

_____

(continued on next page)

3. _____

_____

D. CROSSWORD PUZZLE

Our puzzle this week features mostly adjectives and adverbs. We already have the puzzle worked out--your job is to write the clues! Look at the solution on the next page and write a clue for each word. You will probably have to look up some of the words in a dictionary. Clues may be synonyms (use your thesaurus), or a short dictionary definition. We've filled in three clues to help you get started. When your clues are finished, ask someone in your family to work the puzzle.

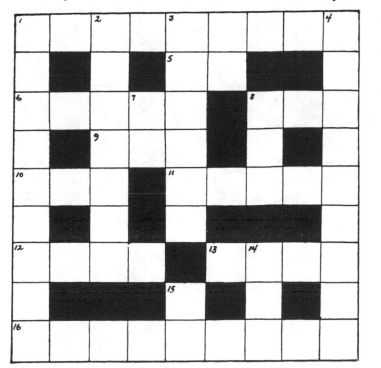

Down:

1. _____

2. _____

3. _____

4. _____

7. ___ ♥ ___ _____

8. _____

14. _____

15. _____

Across:

1. _____

5. _____

6. _____

8. _____

9. _____

10. _____

11. _____

12. _Sung on Old McDonald's farm_

13. _Good (in Italian)_

16. _____

IMAGINATION STRETCHER:

Use the grid below to construct your own crossword puzzle! To make it more interesting, choose a theme for your puzzle, such as "a day at the beach" or "the night sky." The words don't all have to be adjectives or adverbs, but most of them should be related to the theme. Trace the grid on white paper and write your solution. Black out the unused squares and number the squares that begin words. Then write your clues and ask a friend to solve the puzzle.

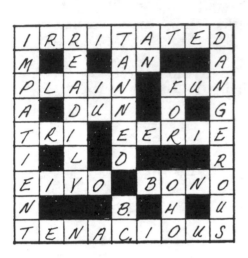

Across:

_____

_____

_____

_____

_____

_____

Down:

_____

_____

_____

_____

_____

_____

I COMPLETED THIS ASSIGNMENT ON _____.

WORDS AND WEATHER GO TOGETHER

Have you ever done any weather reporting? The first step is to look out the window! Write three adjectives that describe what the weather is like today:

Today is _____, _____, and _____.

Of course, weather changes all the time. We'll write a "weather report" that predicts a change, but our report will be a little out of the ordinary. The reason is, it will be a poem seven lines long. (Our editor likes poetic weather reports.)

Follow these instructions:

On line 1, write one noun that names the main feature of today's weather (sun, drizzle, clouds, heat, etc.)
On line 7, write what you think might happen tomorrow (as long as it's not the same thing).
On lines 2 and 6, write two adjectives that describe each day. (If you can't go outside and experience the weather, imagine how these conditions would feel, smell and sound.)
On lines 3 and 5, write three action verbs ending in "-ing."
On line 4, write two simple sentences (subject-verb) that make the transition from one kind of weather to the next.

Here's an example:

```
            Wind
        Gusty, Chilly
    Tearing, chasing, booming;
 Wind  pauses,  clouds  gather;
 Dripping, pelting, drenching,
        Steady, dreary
            Rain.
```

This form of poetry is called "diamante" because of its shape. What is that shape?

Write a diamante poem forecasting a change in the weather. Follow the directions above for each line.

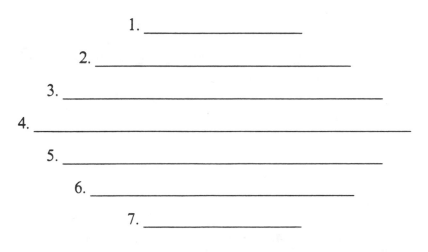

1. _____

2. _____

3. _____

4. _____

5. _____

6. _____

7. _____

I COMPLETED THIS ASSIGNMENT ON _____.

A "diamante" poem is a poem written in a diamond shape. Let's write one more weather-based diamante poem, with a few differences in the directions.

What's your favorite outdoor activity? Write it here:

_____

On Line 1, write an adjective (not a noun this time) describing the perfect weather for this activity. On Line 7, write an adjective describing the worst weather. Complete the poem with these directions:

Line 2: Write two adjectives describing how the weather on Line 1 looks, smells, sounds, or feels.
Line 6: Write two adjectives describing how the weather on Line 7 looks, smells, sounds, or feels.
Lines 3 and 5: Write a noun (or pronoun), a verb and an adverb showing how people move in the two kinds of weather (such as, "we skip lightly," or "skaters glide smoothly").
Line 4: Write one simple sentence of four or five words, showing how the weather changes.

1. _____

2. _____

3. _____

4. _____

5. _____

6. _____

7. _____

I COMPLETED THIS ASSIGNMENT ON _____.

Adjectives and adverbs are the easy modifiers. Next we'll look at another type of modifier that may be a little more difficult. That's because it's not a single word; it's a group of words. We call it a *prepositional phrase*.

PREPOSITIONS: PUNY WORDS WITH POWERFUL PURPOSE

Not all "little" words are prepositions, and some prepositions are not all that little. Here are some of the most common prepositions:

above	at	beside	from	up
across	before	between	in	with
against	behind	by	into	through
among	below	for	of	under

The word "to" is often used as a preposition, but not always! You've already learned that "to" can be used with verbs. The important thing to remember is that if "to" appears with a verb, it is *not* a preposition.

The job of a preposition is to turn a noun into a modifier. Prepositions never stand alone, but always form **prepositional phrases**.

The noun that a preposition "grabs" is called the **object of the preposition.** That object can have any number of adjectives, and the adjectives are part of the prepositional phrase, too. Here are some examples:

Preposition	Adjective(s)	Noun
in	the deep, dark, crawly	basement
with	loud, excited	squeals
on	the hot, gritty	sand

Add a couple of adjectives to these phrases:

1. with the _____, _____ clown

2. for the _____, _____ teacher

3. about the _____, _____ story

And now make up some prepositional phrases of your own, using one preposition, one adjective, and one noun.:

Preposition	adjective	noun

1. _____

2. _____

3. _____

I COMPLETED THIS EXERCISE ON _____.

FAMILY PHOTOS FOSTER FOND RECOLLECTIONS

Find three photographs of you and your family or friends and paste them in the spaces below and on the next page. If you don't have any photos, you may draw your own pictures about things that really happened to you.

On the first line below each picture, write a declarative sentence with a subject, a verb, and an object--nothing else! It will be very short.

Example: Dad caught a bass.

On line 2, write the same sentence, but add one or two prepositional phrases.

Example: Dad caught a bass <u>in Mystic Lake</u>.

On line 3, write the sentence again, adding two adjectives and one adverb. That will be your final caption.

Example: <u>Today,</u> Dad caught a <u>huge</u> bass in <u>beautiful</u> Mystic Lake.

1. _____

2. _____

3. _____

_____

1. _____

2. _____

3. _____

_____

1. _____

2. _____

3. _____

_____

I COMPLETED THIS ASSIGNMENT ON _____.

PRACTICE MAKES PERFECT, EDITOR INSISTS

Because the sentence is the basic unit of writing, a writer must understand how it is put together. The following exercises will give you a little more practice in recognizing and using modifiers.

The following three news articles were submitted by one of our reporters. Read the first two carefully and notice that all the prepositional phrases are underlined. The circled words are either nouns or verbs. The arrows from each prepositional phrase point to the word it modifies.

How can you tell whether a prepositional phrase modifies a noun or a verb? Here are some hints to help you tell the difference.

A prepositional phrase modifies a verb if
It tells when, where, how or how much something happened.

```
Sally walked to the park. (Tells where)
With a sigh, Jo answered the phone. (Tells how)
School ended before noon. (Tells when)
```

A prepositional phrase modifies a noun if

    a. It shows possession (look for the preposition "of").

```
the beauty of a sunset        the Acts of the Apostles
```

    b. It helps describe a noun.

```
the girl with pigtails          a coat of wool
```

    c. It is connected to another prepositional phrase.

```
on the table with the books

a picture of the bride in the newspaper
```

Just read the first article and notice how prepositional phrases work.

Jerry Spencer, who (lives) on Brady Avenue, has agreed to serve as (Cubmaster) for Pack 387. Mr. Spencer will (begin) his duties on August 22 at the Pack's first (meeting) of the year. All (boys) of ages 6-8 are invited to attend.

In the second article, the prepositional phrases are underlined but you will find the noun or verb that each phrase modifies. Circle the word and draw arrows from the phrase.

Mr. and Mrs. Herbert McBride announce the engagement of their daughter, Laura, and Mr. Larry Ferguson, of Spokane, Washington. The couple will wed at First Community Church on February 14. They plan to honeymoon in Palm Springs, then make their home in Cedar Lake.

In the next article, underline all the prepositional phrases. Then circle the word that each phrase modifies, and draw an arrow from the phrase to the word.

Mr. Wayne Endicott, a long-time resident of Jonesville, wants an interesting proposition on the November ballot. He believes that roller-skating should be allowed on city streets and in local malls. "I could complete my shopping in half the time," he claims. On local radio programs, at public gatherings, and in shopping centers, he promotes his message and collects signatures. "I will reach my goal through sheer persistence," he says.

The city council is not impressed. "This idea of Mr. Endicott's is absurd," says Mayor Sheila O'Leary. "Not everyone is a responsible skater. How many innocent citizens will end up in the hospital because they were hit by reckless rollers? As far as we're concerned, this proposal is under a cloud."

I COMPLETED THIS EXERCISE ON _____.

NEWSPAPER STAFF WRITERS REVIEW SENTENCES

Let's pause a moment and review what we've learned about words and sentences.

When we put sentences together, all words fall into groups called **parts of speech**. These groups have very little to do with what each word means (its definition). Instead, they refer to the *function* of each word in the sentence. In a good sentence, all words are "working" words--every one has a job to do.

You have learned all eight parts of speech and the job that each one performs in a sentence. Here is the list:

Noun: Names a person, place, thing or idea. Nouns are the "busiest" words in a sentence because they can take several positions. The subject and the object of a sentence are both nouns, or words that substitute for nouns. The object of a preposition is also a noun (see "Preposition," below).
Pronoun: Substitutes for a noun. May be placed anywhere in the sentence that a noun could go. The most common pronouns are *he, she, it, they, we,* and *you.* Pronouns that show possession, like *my, his, hers, your, our,* and *their* are used as adjectives. (See "Adjective," below.)
Article: A noun "marker." There are only three: *a, an,* and *the.*
Verb: Shows what the subject of a sentence does or is. **Linking verbs** (such as *is, are, was,* and *were)* link the subject to a complement. **Helping verbs** show a change in time or meaning.
Conjunction: Joins two similar parts of a sentence. *And, but* and *or* are the most common conjunctions. By "similar," we mean that the sentence part joined by a conjunction must be the same kind of part: two subjects, two verbs, etc.
Adjective: Always modifies a noun. By "modify," we mean that it describes or explains in some way.
Adverb: Modifies a verb, adjective or other adverb. When modifying a verb, the adverb tells *when, where,* or *how.* When modifying an adjective or other adverb, it tells *how much.*
Preposition: Joins with a noun or pronoun to make a **prepositional phrase**. The prepositional phrase may modify either a noun or verb.

You should know not only what the parts of speech are, but also how they work together in sentences. Here once again is the basic sentence structure, but shown this time in what we call a sentence "diagram." Study the diagram to make sure you understand how all the parts of speech fit into the basic sentence structure. Then we'll move on.

Today Dad caught a huge bass in beautiful Mystic Lake.

EDITORS AID REPORTERS

Do you remember writing a definition for the verb "edit" on page 24? Look up the definition now if you don't, because we're about to do some editing.

The reporter for the news story below has done well with nouns and verbs but forgot the modifiers. Between the lines, add about 5 adjectives, 3 adverbs and 5 prepositional phrases. These words should make the story more interesting and easier to understand. You will have to imagine a few details. If you don't know anything about clothes (it's a fashion show story), ask an expert or read clothing descriptions in a catalogue or your newspaper style section. Use your Thesaurus to find synonyms for words like "pretty," "attractive," "stunning," or "tall."

The first paragraph is already edited. You are to finish the job.

The Mercy Hospital Fashion Expo was a ^*brilliant* success.
Members of the Hospital staff were models ^*in the show*. The Forest
Room of the Grand Isle Hotel held an ^*enthusiastic* audience of about
450.

Clerks from the Billing Department began the first
half of the show with a collection of coats and jackets.
A floor-length cape drew an extra round of applause.
Nurses' aides then modeled sportswear. Just before
intermission, the entire volunteer staff posed in a winter
sports scene, complete with an artificial snowfall.

The second half began with the ward nurses in winter
suits. The custodial staff, in sports coats and casual
wear, escorted the ladies. The Grand Finale featured
surgical aides and nurses in formal dress. A velvet gown,
a satin dress and a rhinestone vest were highlights. To
end the show, the surgical staff whirled around the stage
in a waltz.

(continued on next page)

A reception followed the show. Comptroller Todd Marshall later stated that the event raised $22,000 for the Hospital.

I COMPLETED THIS ASSIGNMENT ON _____.

ADVERTISING MAKES WORLD GO 'ROUND-- OR DOES IT?

With all the advertising on radio, TV, billboards, posters and grocery shopping carts, it can certainly make our heads go 'round! Perhaps we would all like to see a little less advertising, but newspapers can't get along without it. Most of the money we need to operate comes from businesses who pay to have their ads printed.

Modifiers are very important in advertising. Did you ever notice how the right adjective can make a noun sound good or bad? You may not like snakes, but you'd probably rather meet a "smooth, glistening" snake than a "slimy" one. "Soft, luxurious" armchairs are better than "lumpy" armchairs, and a "friendly" sheepdog makes a better impression than a "slobbering" one. Advertisers would never use words like "slimy," "lumpy" or "slobbering" to sell their products! Nor are they very happy with boring adjectives like "good" and "nice."

For your next assignment, you'll need an apple and a banana, or a slice of each. Take a bite of the apple and chew it slowly and carefully. Think of three words that describe how the apple *tastes* and *feels* in your mouth, and write those words in the chart below. Try not to use adjectives that tell how much you like (or don't like) the apple; words like "delicious" or "scrumptious" or even "yucky." These words can be used to describe any food. What we're looking for is words that will apply to an *apple*. The words we've chosen for an orange should give you an idea.

When that bite is all gone, and the taste of it is out of your mouth, try the banana. As you're chewing, think of three adjectives that will describe a banana, but not an apple, and write them on the chart.

ORANGE	APPLE	BANANA
juicy		
tangy		
cool		

(continued on next page)

You will use these words to write two display ads. A **display ad** is a paid advertisement that takes more space than a classified and often uses pictures to attract more attention. Page through any newspaper and notice the display ads. You'll find that they may be any size, from one inch up to an entire page. Businesses often hire professional advertisers to design the ads for them, and many newspapers and magazines keep designers on staff. In the next few pages, you'll be designing several advertisements using modifiers and imagination.

First, the Blossom Valley Apple Growers and the Cucaracha Banana Company want to promote their products in our newspaper. Each display ad must have a picture of the product and three clear, descriptive adjectives, but the rest is up to you. Use the spaces below to create your design. Fancy lettering, additional artwork and an eye-catching border will help, but the *words* you use are more important than any of those. You may want to try out some ideas in your notebook first before drawing the completed ad.

Hint: Try a combination of declarative, imperative, interrogative and exclamatory sentences (though not necessarily all four of them in one ad!).

I COMPLETED THIS ASSIGNMENT ON _____.

All kinds of retail stores (grocery, hardware, clothing, toys, etc.) run display ads every week to let the public know about the wonderful items they have on sale. What's your favorite store? If that store were holding a COLOSSAL ONCE-IN-A-LIFETIME SALE (!!!), what four items would you most like to see reduced to a price you could afford? Write them on the lines on the next page, using the complete brand name (if you know it) and two adjectives that describe each one. It may be hard to think of *different* adjectives for these items. If you're describing toys, for example, the word "fun" may come to mind more than you'd like. Two hints may help you here:

1) Use your thesaurus
2) Think of some "-ing" verbs, like "thrilling," "amusing" or "exciting." We often use verbs ending in "-ing" as adjectives. These special adjectives are called **participals**.

1. _____

2. _____

3. _____

4. _____

     Now you get to design a half-page display ad for your favorite store! The artwork is entirely up to you this time, and if you don't think much of your drawing ability, don't worry--just sketch in your ideas. The words are important here, not the artwork.

     The words, phrases and sentences that will go into the ad are called **copy**. Your job is to write copy that will attract the reader's attention. You must include the name and address of the store (look it up in the phone book) and the four items you listed above, with their descriptive adjectives and the sale prices (that's *very* important). Once again, try out your design in your notebook before drawing it below. If the ideas just don't seem to be coming, look through the ads of your local newspaper for inspiration.

I COMPLETED THIS ASSIGNMENT ON _____.

Did you know that churches run display ads? Churches are not in business to make money, of course, but they want to invite newcomers, visitors and seekers into their fellowship. Try to find the church ads in your local newspaper--if it's a daily paper you should find them in the "Religion" section on Saturday. Many of these ads use well-known symbols (such as a cross, a fish, praying hands, etc.) with words that express how the church wants to be seen by the community. Notice that the tone is different from the ads of many stores and other businesses. What do you think makes that difference?

Think of three adjectives that describe the things you like best about your church, and write them in the left column. Then use them to design an attractive but dignified display ad. Be sure to include the address of your church, with morning worship and Sunday school times.

My church is

_____

_____

_____

I COMPLETED THIS ASSIGNMENT ON _____.

EFFECTIVE ADS LAUNCH REAL ESTATE BOOM

Real estate ads, like display ads, often take up a lot of space and include a picture of the house to be sold. But the copy reads like a classified: a list of special features, a price, an agent's name, a telephone number, and not many complete sentences. Real estate agencies often group several of these individual classifieds in one big display ad under the name of the company or agent.

The copy for each is written by the agent who wants to sell the house. Naturally, he or she will include the most attractive features of the house and ignore the features that aren't so nice. Find and read some real estate ads in your local paper. How does the agent make the property sound attractive? Do you find certain adjectives and exclamations used over and over again? What are some words that make you suspect the property is not in good shape?

If you had to sell your own house, what words would you use? In the "Idea Box" on the next page, write three features of your home that you think buyers might like, using one or two adjectives for each. In the "For Sale" Box, write your advertisement and draw a picture of the property beside it. You are allowed only forty words or less, including the price and the agent's name and phone number. Make them count!   We've done the first ad for you as an example.

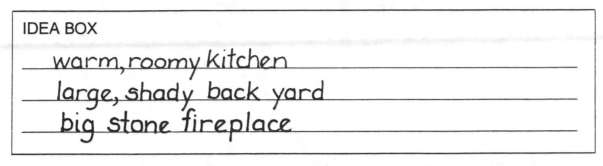

IDEA BOX

warm, roomy kitchen
large, shady back yard
big stone fireplace

FOR SALE:

Wonderful family home! Summer fun in large, shady back yard, winter comfort beside big stone fireplace. Check out this roomy kitchen! 3 bedrooms, 1½ baths. Only $30,000. Come and look! Tina, 555-0123.

Now sell your house in only forty words or less:

IDEA BOX

_____

_____

_____

FOR SALE:

_____

_____

_____

_____

_____

And now sell your favorite restaurant in forty words or less. Your possible buyer will want to know about more than the building itself. The location and the number of customers are also important.

IDEA BOX

_____

_____

_____

FOR SALE:

_____

_____

_____

_____

_____

I COMPLETED THIS ASSIGNMENT ON _____.

IMAGINATION STRETCHERS

Pretend you are a real estate agent. Write ads in your notebook offering any two of the following "properties" for sale:

The White House   Your dream treehouse
The Cottage of the Three Bears   The Sahara Desert
Gettysburg Battlefield   The Statue of Liberty

I COMPLETED THESE TWO EXERCISES ON _____.

EXOTIC DESTINATIONS LURE ARMCHAIR TRAVELERS

Advertising copy is written for one purpose: to attract users or buyers. But newspapers are not all advertising, of course. People read newspapers to learn what's going on in our big wide world. Most big-city newspapers devote an entire section to travel, for those readers who dream of going to faraway places. The travel section is usually part of the Sunday paper.

Look through the travel section of your local paper. You'll see that it contains articles by writers who have (for example) walked on the Great Wall of China, or tried all the pastry shops in Vienna, Austria, or know the best ski resorts in Utah. Alongside these articles you'll find advertisements for cruise ships, travel agencies and special tours. The ads will only tell you the good stuff, of course. But a good travel writer will also share the low points, such as the poor service at a particular hotel, or the rubbery fish served on the cruise ship, or the scenery that didn't live up to expectations.

Travel writers, unlike advertisers, use adjectives to **qualify** an object or experience. This means that they will try to explain what is good *and* not so good about it. It's easy to see the difference when you compare advertising with other types of writing. In the two examples below, which is the advertisement?

The Smith County Historical Museum offers something for everyone. Youngsters will love the Generations Room, where they can dress up in authentic costume, play with the sturdy toys of yesteryear, and even build a life-size teepee! Fascinating hands-on exhibits--from lifelike dioramas to exciting computer quizzes--make our state's history come alive. Where else can the whole family spend a fun-filled afternoon for only $5.00?

The Smith County Historical Museum is a mixed treat. The kids are bound to enjoy the famous Generations Room, which is neat and well-staffed with friendly, informative guides. Other exhibits are interesting, especially the new computer quizzes. But the Indian Life room should be completely redone; even the lighting seems dusty. We also thought it was time to change some of the dioramas. Still, the Museum is a bargain at the $5.00 family rate.

The advertisement, as you probably guessed, is on the left. The other piece was written by a visitor giving an honest judgment of what she thought of the Museum. Now, it's your turn!

Imagine that your back yard, or a nearby playground, is an amusement park: the kind that charges admission. If you can't imagine why anybody would *pay* to play on the swings or teeter-totter, pretend you live in a place that never heard of bumper cars, roller-coasters or Disney World. Think of an exciting name for your "park" and write an ad for it in the box on the next page. Just write the ad copy--no pictures this time. Remember, you are the owner of this park and you want customers.

_____

_____

_____

_____

_____

Now imagine that you are a travel writer. On the lines below, write about the day you spent at the amusement park. Think about these questions before you start writing: Was it as fun as the ad promised it would be? What "ride" did you enjoy most? Were the grounds clean and attractive? Did you buy any food? Was it above average or nothing special? What, if anything, disappointed you about the park? If a friend of yours wanted to go, would you advise him or her to save the money? Why or why not? Write at least four sentences on the subject.

_____

_____

_____

_____

_____

_____

_____

_____

When you're finished, read what you've written and circle the words or groups of words that express your opinion about the place you visited.

I COMPLETED THIS ASSIGNMENT ON _____.

Let's write another travel piece about a familiar place.

Many homes are called "historic landmarks" because they are very old, or because something important happened there, or because someone who later became famous grew up there. Use your imagination again and pretend that someone famous grew up in your house--maybe it was you! Write about a tour of your house as if it were an historic landmark. If you can persuade someone in your family to give you a "tour," this will probably be more interesting.

Your readers will want to know:

Why the house is famous
One specific thing that you found interesting
What you liked or didn't like about the tour guide
Why you would (or would not) recommend this tour to others

Write at least five sentences on the page below, then think of a headline to write at the top:

_____

I COMPLETED THIS ASSIGNMENT ON _____.

That's enough pretending. This time we'll write about a real tourist attraction.

You may live near an actual historic landmark, a theme park or amusement park, or a recreation area. Even if you don't live nearby, you've probably visited such a place. On the next page write a travel piece about it, based on what you remember. Be clear about what you enjoyed or didn't enjoy about your visit (and *why*). Let your reader know what to expect, how to dress, and how long to plan on staying. Tell about one thing you especially liked, and another thing that might have been done better.

Try to fill up the page, and don't forget the headline!

_____

_____

_____

_____

_____

_____

_____

_____

_____

_____

_____

_____

_____

_____

I COMPLETED THIS ASSIGNMENT ON _____.

READING REVIEWERS HIT BOOKS

Our editor is always looking for **reviews**. This is another kind of writing that *qualifies* (tells what is good or bad about) a subject. Most newspapers print reviews of movies, plays, books, and TV programs, to help readers decide if they want to see that show or read that book.

Reviewers are supposed to be honest about their judgments--an unfavorable review of a book, for instance, ought to be based on the bad qualities of the book, and not on the fact that the reviewer does not like the author. A "rave" review of a movie should be concerned with the quality of the movie itself, and not with the star's beautiful smile.

Besides being honest and fair, a reviewer should be specific. Read the two reviews below and decide which is more helpful to a reader:

COLUMN ONE

Prince Caspian, by C. S. Lewis, is the exciting story of a boy who wins his rightful kingdom back from his evil uncle. Caspian is a believable character, an ordinary boy who starts out shy and frightened but grows into a strong and confident king with the help of many friends. My favorite character is Reepicheep, a mouse who is not "mousy" at all! Mr. Lewis describes the imaginary country of Narnia as clearly as though he were taking a walk through it. It's a place we can easily imagine, although there were times when I wished he would stop describing and get on with the story. The conversations between the characters are often very funny. Reading this book makes me want to go have an adventure!

COLUMN TWO

Prince Caspian is a very good book. The story is exciting and the characters are interesting. The descriptions are good, too. I liked it.

It's easy to see that the review in Column One is more interesting, but it's also much more helpful to someone who may want to read the book Why is that? Look at the review in Column Two again. If you put the title of your favorite book in the first sentence, the same words could be used. In fact, the same words could apply to *any* book you may happen to like, from *Babar and Celeste* to *Nancy Drew and the Hidden Staircase* to *Gone With the Wind!*

Here are some of the things a writer must consider when writing a book review:

Story	Exciting, fast-moving, interesting, slow, surprising
Characters	Real, funny, dull, interesting, unusual, flat (not like a pancake, but like a landscape--always the same)
Description	Sharp, clear, dull, over-long
Language	Funny, interesting, clever, sparkling, monotonous (boring), unique (like nothing else you've read), old-fashioned, hard-to-follow

We hope this gives you an idea of what makes a good review, because now you're going to write one. Write a short review of the last fictional book you read. (A fictional book tells a story that didn't really happen.) Remember, this will be a review, not a report. What's the difference? A report tells what the book is *about*. A review tells *how good* the book is--or at least, how good the reviewer thinks it is-- and why.

This will be easier if we break it into steps.

STEP ONE: Use the list of adjectives on the previous page to help you think about the different elements of the book. You may circle some of the suggested adjectives you would like to use, or get out your thesaurus and look up some different ones.

STEP TWO: Write a sentence on the lines below that contains the book title, the author's name, and a brief statement of what the book is about. You may use the first sentence in Column One of the previous page as a model.

STEP THREE: Write three or four sentences expressing your judgment about the characters, story, etc. Try not to start all your sentences the same way, such as: "The characters were . . ." "The language is. . ."

STEP FOUR: Write a concluding sentence that expresses your overall feelings about the book. If you've done a good job, the sentences in the middle should make it clear why you feel that way.

STEP FIVE: Finally, write a headline. And that's another assignment finished!

I COMPLETED THIS ASSIGNMENT ON _____.

PART III:

ORGANIZING AND REPORTING

Remember the first step for any kind of writing? Before you write anything -- THINK! Get ready to do a lot of thinking in this part of the book.

In the first two parts of this book you learned how to make sentences out of words. In this last part you'll learn how to make paragraphs out of sentences. If you have been reading books for a few years, you already understand something about how an author groups sentences together in paragraphs. You'll understand much better, of course, after you've written several paragraphs of your own!

As a reporter you will learn to gather information, organize it and express it in clear sentences that our readers can understand. Once you can do that, all kinds of writing opportunities could open up for you--you might even find yourself doing some of our editor's job.

Speaking of the editor, you're wanted in his office. He'll explain what a paragraph is...

PARAGRAPH PRINCIPLES TAKE PRACTICE

Every paragraph should be written to serve a purpose. That doesn't mean that every time you sit down to write you'll have to say to yourself, "Paragraph One will be for _____, and I'll write Paragraph Two for _____." Experienced writers can plan paragraphs without thinking too hard about them. But beginning writers probably need a little practice in recognizing how paragraphs are put together, and what purposes they serve.

One way to figure out the purpose of a particular paragraph is to find the **topic sentence.** This is the sentence that seems to state most clearly what the paragraph is about. Often you'll find the topic sentence at the beginning of the paragraph, but sometimes it's at the end, or maybe even somewhere in the middle.

Underline the topic sentences in each paragraph of this news story. The first one is done for you; you'll find answers to the rest on page A.

The first meeting of the Stop Whining And Participate (SWAP) Society was a great success. Over 25 interested citizens met in the library conference room on Saturday afternoon. The meeting was called to order by acting president Russell Spivey, who immediately asked for suggestions for a statement of purpose.

After much discussion, the Society's statement was approved. According to the statement, the purpose of SWAP is "to work together to improve our community by positive actions instead of complaints."

Next, the Society discussed activities for the group. Visits to retirement homes, Christmas baskets for the less fortunate, a job training service for teenagers from needy families, and after-school clubs were suggested. All of these are services that would benefit our community. A committee was formed to look into these and other possibilities.

At the next meeting the SWAP Society will elect officers and choose one project to begin working on. All interested citizens are encouraged to attend the meeting on April 17 at 1:30 in the Library Conference Room. SWAP needs you!

In the three paragraphs below, the topic sentence is missing. You'll understand what each paragraph is about by reading the rest of the sentences. Try to write a topic sentence that will tie all the sentences together and state the subject clearly. The first topic sentence is already filled-in; use it as an example.

1. *Making a peanut butter sandwich is easy and fun.*
First you get two slices of bread. Spread one of the slices with peanut butter, just thick enough so the sandwich won't be too squashy. Most people prefer to use jelly on the other slice of bread, but honey is a yummy substitute, or sliced bananas. You can be creative but I would not suggest mustard. Put the two slices together and take a big bite.

2. _____

_____

The tree must not be too tall or there won't be room to put the star on top. Full trees look beautiful, but if it's too full getting it through the front door will be difficult! Also, ornaments will not hang properly unless there is some space between the branches.

    3. The nurse rubbed my arm with an alcohol swab that felt like a cold finger. The sharp smell stung my nose. I could feel my muscles tensing up. "This will only hurt for a second," she promised. I was thinking of weeks of agony when the needle went in. Ouch!

_____

_____.

I COMPLETED THESE EXERCISES ON _____.

REPORTERS SHARPEN SKILLS AS EDITORS

    Before *you* write some paragraphs, let's do a little more editing. The four paragraphs below are ready to go into the newspaper, except for one thing: the reporter always leaves in one sentence that doesn't belong. It may be a perfectly good sentence, with a subject and verb and all the modifiers in the right place. The problem is that it doesn't seem to fit with the rest of the sentences. Remember, a paragraph is a group of sentences that work together to express one idea, or create one picture. Find and underline the one sentence in each of the paragraphs below that doesn't help the other sentences. We've done the first one for you. Remaining answers are on page B.

1.   Mayor Thomas arrived for our interview promptly at 1:30. He is a large man but his movements reminded me of a puppy. He was always bouncing up in his seat to shake hands with someone, or waving at people on the other side of the room. <u>He was elected by a landslide two years ago.</u> Even while talking to me, his eyes never stopped glancing in every direction.

2.   First Community Church's production of "The Littlest Angel" last Thursday evening was a delight. Tickets were $1.50 in advance and $2.00 at the door. Each "little angel" in the cast knew his or her lines perfectly and spoke them with confidence. Carly Sono gave an especially touching performance in the lead role. I'm sure very few eyes were still dry when the play was over.

3.   Neighbors were relieved to learn that an escaped 8-foot rock
python belonging to Claudia Wurst, 2027 Maple Drive, has been found.
Rock pythons are native to central Africa. Ms. Wurst reported her pet
missing on Tuesday, but it was not until late Thursday afternoon that
"Slinky" was discovered coiled around the birdbath in the back yard of
Mr. and Mrs. Fred Gleiss. Ms. Wurst was very glad to get Slinky back.
However, Mrs. Gleiss now reports that her toy Pekinese, Shmaltzy, is
missing.

4.   The "Holiday in Lights" winter show officially opens on the Friday
after Thanksgiving. This is one of my favorite times of the year. I
love the lights, the music, the spicy smells, the shoppers hurrying
along with mysterious packages. But sometimes I wonder if we all hurry
so much that we've forgotten what the season means. Let's all slow down
and think for a moment.

Now that you've marked the sentences that don't belong, think about *why*
they don't belong. In each case, it was because they didn't help the paragraph serve
its purpose.

What is a paragraph's purpose? Here are a few:

> To describe something or someone
> To tell a short story or part of a story
> To explain how to do something
> To convince the reader of something that the writer believes

In the spaces below, write a phrase or sentence that tells what you think the purpose
of each paragraph was. We will tell you the first one. Check your answers on page
B.

#1: <u>To describe the Mayor during an interview.</u>

#2: _____

#3: _____

#4: _____

I COMPLETED THIS EXERCISE ON _____.

Sometimes it's a good idea to "break up" a long paragraph to make it easier
to read. Most long paragraphs can be broken into shorter ones without too much
trouble. Read the three stories below. The first one is divided by a "paragraph
break" symbol. Find a good place to divide the other two paragraphs and indicate
the place with a paragraph break: ¶

---

1.   The Congressmen spent two days debating the crime bill.   The speeches were mostly against the bill during the first day.   The main argument was that the proposed laws were not tough enough on criminals.*¶* By the second day, opinions seemed to be turning in favor of the bill.   Though no one appeared to like everything in it, all agreed that something had to be done about crime.

---

2.   The Beautiful Neighborhood Society has announced the winner of their third annual "Miss Front Yard" contest.   Polly Keller was awarded the crown for her charming "Japanese Garden" arrangement of ponds and waterfalls.   "I'm so thrilled," exclaimed Mrs. Keller.   She receives a $100 gift certificate and a year's supply of Go-Go-Gro plant food for her lovely landscape.   The public is invited to tour her yard at 111 Highpoint Avenue from 2:00-5:00 p.m. on Sunday.

---

3.   Shady Acres Retirement Home will be celebrating an anniversary next week.   The facility opened its doors 25 years ago with rooms for 35 residents.   Today, after two wings were added to the original building, 110 senior citizens call Shady Acres home.   A reception is planned for Saturday, October 23.   The public is invited to stop by from 1:00-4:00 p.m. for refreshments and a tour of the Home.   Sue Davis, program director, expects at least 400 visitors.

I COMPLETED THIS ASSIGNMENT ON _____.

Here's a different kind of editing. The list of sentences below are supposed to be an article of two paragraphs, but they're all mixed up. Can you sort them out?

In the space before each sentence, mark an "A" or a "B" to indicate whether it belongs in the first paragraph or the second. Then, beside each letter, write a number indicating the order of that sentence in the paragraph. You'll have to read all the sentences a few times before you start marking. It would probably be helpful to make a photocopy of this page and cut the sentences apart so you can rearrange them. Check your answers on page B.

__ __	Dogs of 37 different breeds participated in the show.
__ __	After all the excitement, Miss Mange, a Llasa Apso, was awarded Best of Show.
__ __	The Kennel Club Pet Show was a howling success, but not in the way its sponsors intended.
__ __	The Armory Hall resounded to the barks of over one hundred entries.
__ __	Some practical joker set a rabbit loose on the viewing stage during the final judging.
__ __	Huskies, mastiffs, and Indian dholes were some of the many breeds observed by this reporter.
__ __	The frightened bunny leapt off the viewing stage and tore down the nearest aisle, followed by three prize pups.
__ __	A quick-thinking custodian scooped the rabbit into a cardboard box and out of harm's way.
__ __	The dogs who could not join the chase added their voices to the tremendous din.
__ __	Anxious owners groomed their pets, each hoping to take home the $150 grand prize.

I COMPLETED THIS ASSIGNMENT ON _____.

Now that you have that one straightened out, here's another. This will be more of a challenge because the story should be broken into *three* paragraphs. First decide where each sentence belongs: in Paragraph "A," "B," or "C." Then number the sentences in a logical order. Answers are on page B.

(continued on next page)

__ __	Peering at the nearest duplex, he thought he saw a reflection of flames on a wall.
__ __	Minnie Page, the 76-year-old resident, was asleep in her bedroom.
__ __	Last week, he was just the newspaper boy.
__ __	He pounded on the door but received no answer, so he broke the front window and entered the apartment.
__ __	Jim jumped off his bike and raced to the door of the duplex.
__ __	Young Jim Martins is now known as a hero to his neighbors on 17th Ave.
__ __	"He saved my life," Mrs. Page said later.
__ __	Just before dawn on Wednesday, Jim Martins was completing his route on 99th St.
__ __	Today, he can't complete his route without people stopping to ask about the burning home.
__ __	The smoke alarm had failed to go off, due to a dead battery.
__ __	"I can't thank God enough that Jim was there."
__ __	Jim woke her and led her to safety just moments before she would have succumbed to smoke inhalation.
__ __	Suddenly, he smelled a whiff of smoke.

I COMPLETED THIS ASSIGNMENT ON _____.

WRITERS AT HOME SHARE RECIPES, HINTS

Our Food Editor, Miss Marvelous, went on vacation this week and left us with the recipe on the next page. We can't figure it out. Can you? If you don't know much about cooking, ask for advice from the main cook in your house. Then write three or four sentences explaining what to do with this stuff. The sentences should make up one paragraph.

MAGIC MYSTERY CASSEROLE

Ingredients: *Procedure:*
1 lb. cooked meat
2 cups cooked rice or pasta   _____
1 can cream soup
1/2 can milk   _____

_____

_____

_____

I COMPLETED THIS ASSIGNMENT ON _____.

We'll need more recipes until the food editor returns from vacation. These can be recipes that you've already tried, or a favorite dish in your family, or something you made up. If you feel adventurous, study the contents of your refrigerator and imagine a dish that could be made from them. Somebody may even like it!

Follow these steps in writing each recipe. It would be a good idea to do steps 1 and 2 in your notebook first, then copy the recipe on the "card" below.

1. List all the ingredients in the order that you will use them, along with the proper amount of each ingredient. Ask for advice from a cook if you're not sure.
2. Write out each step of the recipe in order, and be sure to clearly explain what utensils should be used.
3. Read over the recipe and be sure it makes sense. (It doesn't have to taste good.)
4. Write the name of your recipe on the tab of the "card."

Now, write recipes for:

A HOT DRINK

Ingredients: *Procedure:*

_____   _____

_____   _____

_____   _____

_____   _____

_____   _____

_____   _____

A HEALTHFUL SNACK

Ingredients:

_____

_____

_____

_____

_____

_____

_____

_____

Procedure:

_____

_____

_____

_____

_____

_____

_____

_____

A SALAD

Ingredients:

_____

_____

_____

_____

_____

_____

_____

_____

Procedure:

_____

_____

_____

_____

_____

_____

_____

_____

I COMPLETED THIS ASSIGNMENT ON _____

You're still needed in the Home Section. Miss Marvelous also writes a household hints column under the name Deloris Doit Wright. Our readers are always writing in to ask her how to do certain chores around the house. Some of the following you may already know how to do--if so, this will be easy!

First, make a list of the steps a person must follow to do this job properly. If the question is about something you don't know how to do, you'll have to ask for advice or think a little harder before you write the steps. Next write a paragraph explaining the steps. Add a friendly note at the end of your paragraph, such as, "I hope this helps," or "Have Fun!"

Here's an example of a reader's letter, with Deloris' reply:

```
Dear Deloris,

     My daughter and I have been arguing over the
best way to make a bed.  I told her I would put
the question to you, and we'll agree to do it
the way you suggest.
                         Confused on Maple Ave.
```

Steps: 1. Smooth wrinkles out of bottom sheet.
2. Pull up sheet and smooth out.
3. Pull up and straighten blankets, one by one.
4. Plump up pillows.
5. Pull the bedspread over blankets and pillows and straighten corners.

```
Dear Confused,

     A neatly-made bed starts with the bottom sheet.  Make
sure you pull all the wrinkles out of the bottom sheet
before spreading the top sheet over it.  Then pull up the
blankets and make sure each one is straight and smooth.  The
tops of each blanket should lay in a straight line across
the head of the mattress.  Plump up the pillows and put them
in place.  Finally, pull up the bedspread over the blankets
and pillows and make sure that the spread hangs the same
length from the floor on both sides.  Happy bedmaking!
```

Try your advising skills on these problems:

```
Dear Deloris,

     My cat, Butterball, has been up in a walnut
tree for two days.  The tree is about 25 feet
high and I'm afraid to climb it.  I've tried
coaxing her down with her favorite toys and her
nappy pillow and 14 opened cans of cat food, but
nothing works.  I'm afraid she'll starve to
death up there.  Help!
                         Desperate in Dearborn
```

(continued on next page)

Steps:

_____   _____

_____   _____

_____   _____

Dear Desperate,

_____

_____

_____

_____

_____

_____

_____

_____

I COMPLETED THIS ASSIGNMENT ON _____.

> Dear Deloris,
>
>   Please tell me the best way to get a 10-
> year-old to take out the trash when he's
> supposed to.
>   Frustrated, 120 13th St.

Steps:

_____   _____

_____   _____

_____   _____

Dear Frustrated,

_____

_____

(continued on next page)

_____

_____

_____

_____

_____

I COMPLETED THIS ASSIGNMENT ON _____.

Dear Deloris,

(Whoops! We need another question letter here to fill out the column. Ask someone in your family to write a household hints question that you can answer.)

```
_____

_____

_____

_____

_____

            _____
```

Steps:

_____   _____

_____   _____

_____   _____

Dear _____,

_____

_____

_____

(continued on next page)

_____

_____

_____

_____

_____

I COMPLETED THIS ASSIGNMENT ON _____.

TV VIEWING SIMPLIFIED BY SYNOPSIS SPECIALISTS

Now it's time to go to the Entertainment section. We'll be writing a special kind of paragraph called a **synopsis**.

When you look at the TV page in a newspaper you may notice several short paragraphs (most of them only one sentence long), each explaining what a program is about. The writer of these paragraphs has to "boil down" the plot of the story to a sentence or two so that readers can glance at it and decide whether they want to see the show. That's what a synopsis is: a short re-telling of a story that includes only the most important points.

Which of the paragraphs below is a better synopsis of the familiar story, "Little Red Riding Hood"?

1. A wolf tries to fool a little girl by dressing up as her grandmother. But his evil scheme is defeated, and the good guys win.

2. A little girl shows kindness to her grandmother. She has to overcome some obstacles along the way, but goodness triumphs.

3. Little Red Riding Hood is the story of a mean wolf who gets what's coming to him. A woodcutter saves the day.

4. Little Red Riding Hood is not too smart because she can't tell her grandmother from a wolf in the bed.

5. Little Red Riding Hood is a dumb story because people can't talk to wolves.

The best synopsis is #1, because all the main characters are mentioned, along with the high point of the story. All the other examples are missing something: #2 leaves out the wolf; #3 makes no mention of Red Riding Hood or her grandmother; #4 includes all three main characters but says little about the story; #5 misses the point. The last two seem to be about what the writer *thinks* of the story, rather than the story itself.

Circle the number of the best synopsis of each of these two well-known stories. Check page B for the answer.

THE THREE BEARS

1. Papa Bear, Mama Bear, and Baby Bear live in a cozy house in the woods. One day they go for a walk.

2. A nosy little girl walks into a strange house in the woods and tries out the food and furniture. But she gets the surprise of her life when the owners--three big bears--return.

3. Goldilocks tries three chairs, three beds, and three bowls of porridge. She always likes Baby Bear's stuff the best.

DAVID AND GOLIATH

1. Saul did not believe David could defeat the giant because David was so young. But he let him try anyway.

2. "You come to me with spear and javelin," David said in a clear, ringing voice. "But I come to you by the power of the living God!" Then he threw a stone and Goliath fell down.

3. David and Goliath is the story of a young shepherd boy with a mighty faith. By the power of God he was able to kill a giant with a single stone flung from a slingshot.

I COMPLETED THIS EXERCISE ON _____.

The following stories are going to be produced by our local movie company. You probably know these stories, but you must assume that our readers have never heard of them.

First write a synopsis of two sentences in length that tells what each story is about. Remember to include the major characters and the high point of the story. However, since we want our readers to watch the show, let's not tell them *everything*. Then add one more sentence that will make them wonder how the story ends. Interrogative sentences are good for this.

EXAMPLE:

Cinderella

> A sweet and beautiful girl is treated badly by her mean stepmother, who keeps her from going to the prince's ball. Her fairy godmother comes to her rescue and the prince falls in love with her at the ball. But disaster threatens when Cinderella fails to get home by midnight.

1.   The Midnight Ride of Paul Revere

_____

_____

_____

_____

_____

_____

2.   The Good Samaritan

_____

_____

_____

_____

_____

_____

_____

3.   Snow White and the Seven Dwarfs

_____

_____

_____

_____

_____

_____

I COMPLETED THIS ASSIGNMENT ON _____

Word is going around that you're just about to be promoted to reporter! It's probably true, but there's one more project you'll have to complete.

IT'S CONTEST TIME!

Every few months the newspaper sponsors a contest for its readers. This is a great way to stir up interest and support for the paper, and it's fun for the community, too. We sponsor all kinds of contests--here are a few, just to give you an idea:

Writing	Art	Naming	Games
· essay	· cartoon	· name a sports	· solve a puzzle
· story	· photog-	team, a cartoon	· write a puzzle
· poetry	raphy	character, a new	
	· illustra-	product, etc.	
	tion		

. . . plus recipe contests, and many more. As you may have guessed, you're going to be our next contest coordinator. This will including planning, designing, and writing. We'll break it down into steps for you.

STEP ONE. Decide on the kind of contest this will be. You may already have an idea from the list above. For more ideas, look through other newspapers and magazines. You may even find a book of contests at your local library--ask at the reference desk.

STEP TWO. Work out the details. Here are the items you should consider:

Deadline: _____

Prizes (We can offer up to $300 in cash, goods or services, or you may wish to propose a totally different kind of prize.)

First: _____

Second: _____

Third: _____

Runners-up: _____

Entry rules (Explain clearly how participants are to enter, including details such as the size of the paper, the type of pen to use, who may not enter, etc. Try to answer any question you could possibly be asked about this contest.)

_____

_____

_____

_____

_____

I COMPLETED THIS PART OF THE ASSIGNMENT ON _____.

STEP THREE. Design a 1/2 page display ad. You should include one paragraph explaining what the contest is all about--make it sound like so much fun that everyone will want to enter. Draw or clip some sort of illustration, write a list of rules, and design an entry blank for contestants to fill out.

That's it--until the entries start pouring in!

I COMPLETED THIS PART OF THE ASSIGNMENT ON _____.

You've done several kinds of writing, and each has taught you something about words, sentences, or paragraphs. Now you will be putting all your knowledge together to write news stories. That means you're a reporter!

NEW REPORTERS GO BUZZING AROUND TOWN

The "Buzz Around Town" column is empty--you're about to fill it up! This feature informs our readers of the events that are going on around them--club meetings, exhibits, lectures, music or dance recitals, or any other occasion open to the public.

Is anything going on in your neighborhood? Or anything you would *like* to see going on in your neighborhood?

Think of four events that will take place in your life during the next month, such as birthday parties, scout meetings, school field trips, hikes, or campouts. It doesn't have to be an organized activity. If your family is planning a trip to the zoo next Saturday, write it up. (Family outings are usually not open to the public, but we'll stretch a point in this case.) As you think of these four events, fill out the information on the "Five W's" chart below. You'll find one event filled in already.

WHAT?	WHO?	WHEN?	WHERE?	WHY?
3rd chess match	Todd & Maryl	Tuesday, Oct. 12	Todd's basement, 1221 W. Oak	to determine best chess player in 2 out of 3
1.				
2.				
3.				
4.				

I COMPLETED THIS EXERCISE ON _____.

Once you have your information, you must write it out in proper sentences-- no fewer than two, no more than three. The item about the chess match was written three times. In each paragraph, underline the answers to the 5 "W" questions. The editor is deciding which version he likes best. What is your opinion?

1. There will be a chess match between Maryl Brown and Todd Kinghoven on Tuesday afternoon, October 12, in the Kinghoven basement at 1221 W. Oak Street. This game will determine the winner of two out of three matches.

2.   Maryl Brown and Todd Kinghoven will face off in the last
of three chess matches, to be played in the basement of the
Kinghoven home, 1221 W. Oak Street, on Tuesday afternoon,
October 12. Each player has won one game.

3.   Who is the best chess player on West Oak Street--Maryl
Brown or Todd Kinghoven? Each has won a game. They will
play the deciding match this Tuesday afternoon, October 12,
in Todd's basement at 1221 W. Oak St.

     All of these may give you ideas for writing your own paragraph. Write two
or three sentences for each event you described on the previous page, and try not to
let all the sentences sound alike.

1. _____

_____

_____

_____

_____

2. _____

_____

_____

_____

_____

3. _____

_____

_____

_____

_____

4. _____

_____

(continued on next page)

_____

_____

_____

I COMPLETED THIS ASSIGNMENT ON _____.

IMAGINATION STRETCHERS

Write about two more events you wish you could see in your neighborhood. Use your imagination to fill in a "Five-W" chart in your notebook, then write your paragraphs. If this is something that *could* happen, maybe it will.

I COMPLETED THIS ASSIGNMENT ON _____.

REPORTERS WRITE NEWS BRIEFS WITH NO GRIEF

The Buzz Around Town column is about events that haven't happened yet. Now you'll start reporting on things that have happened, and add another question to the five "W's." The question is:

HOW?

In news reporting, at least four of the five "W's" are usually answered first. That takes only a couple of sentences, as you discovered. Sometimes the "Why?" question is answered later but that still leaves a lot of space. So the rest of the story is taken up with answering "How?" *How* was the pet show disrupted? *How* did Jim Martins save Mrs. Page from the fire? Most of the details in a news story will answer this question.

Our "News Briefs" column contains several short articles about happenings around town. Most of them are only one paragraph long. You'll be writing some News Briefs for us soon, but first, for practice (and for fun), try completing the imaginary "Briefs" beginning on the next page.

The first sentence in each will answer three of the six questions, but you will have to answer the rest. We can't tell you what happened--that's what you'll have to tell us! Think it through before you write anything: what do you think is going on here? Write a paragraph of about five sentences to tell the story.

The first of these stories has already been completed. You may use it as an example for finishing the rest.

where?   when?   who?
While shopping at Bargain City last Saturday, Abby
what?
Resnik received the surprise of her life. *She brought*
some clothing to the checkout counter and gave her
credit card to the clerk. The clerk said, "That's funny.
I used to baby-sit a little girl named Abby Resnik. But
that was back in Michigan." "You're kidding!" exclaimed
Abby. "I grew up in Michigan." It turns out that the
two young ladies did know each other ten years ago
and 800 miles away. They got together for lunch
and laughed over old times.

when?   where?
Three minutes after the Superbowl game began in Miami
what?
Sunday afternoon, an Unidentified Flying Object landed in
the middle of the field.

I COMPLETED THIS ASSIGNMENT ON _____.

who?
    Mrs. Selma Jameson was very surprised when she opened
where?   when?
the dryer in her basement on Monday morning. _____

_____

_____

_____

_____

_____

_____

_____

I COMPLETED THIS ASSIGNMENT ON _____.

who?
    Dr. Hiram Chu, world-renowned marine biologist, has
what?
observed some peculiar behavior among the dolphins off the
where?
coast of Oregon. _____

_____

_____

_____

_____

_____

_____

_____

_____

I COMPLETED THIS ASSIGNMENT ON _____.

NEWSHOUNDS SNIFF OUT STORIES CLOSE TO HOME

After writing those stories, your next assignment will seem easy! Think of three interesting events that have happened around your home or neighborhood in the last month. You may think that nothing interesting ever happens to you, but here at the newspaper we believe that life itself is interesting, if you know how to look at it. So "look" into your memory. Have any of these things happened to you recently?

```
a party                        somebody learned a lesson
an accident (minor, we hope)   somebody made me happy
some good news                 we laughed and laughed when_____
a visit from a relative        I got really mad about _____
a special church service       I was embarrassed when____
```

Choose three recent events in your life to report to the newspaper. Write the "Five W's plus How" of your News Briefs in the following boxes.

1. Event: _____

WHO:
WHAT:
WHEN:
WHERE:
WHY:
HOW:

2. Event: _____

WHO:
WHAT:
WHEN:
WHERE:

(continued on next page)

WHY:	
HOW:	

3. Event: _____

WHO:	
WHAT:	
WHEN:	
WHERE:	
WHY:	
HOW:	

I COMPLETED THIS ASSIGNMENT ON _____.

All you have to do now is write the stories in your notebook. Items for the "News Briefs" column do not need a headline, but you may include a short heading or title if you wish.

Each of the Briefs will be about five to seven sentences long. As usual, four of the Five-W questions should be answered in the first two sentences. The rest of the story will answer "How?" and "Why?"

Write the date you finished each News Brief in the spaces below.

I COMPLETED #1 ON _____.

I COMPLETED #2 ON _____.

I COMPLETED #3 ON _____.

REPORTERS FIND FUNNIES FASCINATING

What's your favorite newspaper feature? If you're like most people your age (or even older) the answer is, "the comics." The first regular comic strip was printed in the *New York World* newspaper about 100 years ago, and since then hundreds of strips have come and gone. You probably have your favorites.

Looking at the comics is a good way to learn about **dialogue**. Dialogue (or dialog) is simply writing what people actually say when they talk. When you're writing about people, dialogue usually adds interest to what you have to say.

In the comics, dialogue is usually shown inside the "balloons" above the characters' heads. In stories and other types of writing, dialogue is indicated by **quotation marks**. These are the little symbols that look like twin tails ("). You should find one quotation mark at the beginning of a quote, and the other at the end. Here's an easy exercise that will give you some practice with quotation marks.

Choose three comic strips in your local newspaper. Cut these out and fasten them to the rectangles below with tape or glue. With a red or blue ink pen, draw quotation marks at the beginning and at the end of the statement in each balloon. It should look something like this:

1.

2.

3.

I COMPLETED THIS EXERCISE ON _____.

On the lines on the next page, write a paragraph describing what's going on in each strip. Use adjectives and adverbs to tell how the characters look and how they seem to feel, and include some (not all) of the dialogue. *Everything that is said in the strip should be inside quotation marks.*

Example:

```
        A patient is in a hospital bed, looking glum
because his elbow won't unbend.  The doctor is
poking his elbow.  "Does it hurt here?" he asks.
He pokes in a painful spot and the patient's arm
whips out and knocks the doctor to the floor.
"Wham!"  From the floor, the doctor says, "That'll
be $65.50 please."
```

On the lines below, write paragraphs describing the three comic strips you cut out.

1. _____

_____

_____

_____

_____

2. _____

_____

_____

_____

_____

3. _____

_____

_____

_____

_____

I COMPLETED THESE PARAGRAPHS ON _____.

Like many bosses, our editor is sometimes talked about. Everyone likes him, but he has a few quirks that some people consider funny. Miss Marvelous is laughing about one of these with "Nose" Numitsky, when You-know-who himself appears. "Nose" feels he has to cover for her. On the panels of the strip, write what you think these people are saying, then draw balloons around each statement.

The strip below was turned in without dialogue. Can you fill in what the characters are saying? Of course, it should be funny. One way to write funny dialogue is to think of a joke (or find one in a joke book) and rewrite it to fit the characters in the strip.

I COMPLETED THIS ASSIGNMENT ON _____

SPORTS WRITERS PRACTICE THEIR "HOOK"

I know you're anxious to return to the sports page! We're interested in all kinds of sports: softball, croquet, tennis, pingpong, even jacks. Your next assignment is to write an article about the last sports activity you watched *or* participated in, whether it was a church volleyball game, a soccer league, or a one-on-one basketball match with your friend in the back yard. We'll even accept a water balloon fight.

We will write the story in steps.

STEP ONE. Choose a sports event to report. Write it on the line below, then write brief answers to the four "W" questions. The Why? and How? will come later.

Event: _____

WHO? _____   WHEN? _____

WHAT? _____   WHERE? _____

STEP TWO. Write your answers to the 4 "W" questions in two sentences.

_____

_____

_____

_____

I COMPLETED THIS ASSIGNMENT ON _____

The sentences you wrote should contain all the necessary information, but now let's think about something besides information.

In the boxes below are two paragraphs written about an exciting sports tournament. They were both submitted to Mr. Flash, our sports editor. Which would you choose to print?

GREENS GRIND SPOTS

The statewide Tiddly-Winks Tournament took place last Thursday evening in the Grand Ballroom of the Hotel Majestic. In the breathtaking final match, the Valley View Greens bested the Maryton Spots by only two points. The Spots put up a valiant defense but they could not stop the final offensive drive of the Greens' top-scoring player, Terry Smith, who put her team over the top with a spectacular two-point shot.

SPOTS DOWNED BY GREENS, 102-104

Tension reigned in the Grand Ballroom of the Hotel Majestic as the Valley View Greens came down to the wire against their opponents, the Marytown Spots. The last match of the annual statewide Tiddly-Winks Tournament was a cliffhanger, with one team, then another, forging ahead. But in the final offensive drive the Greens' top scoring player, Terry Smith, sprang a two-point shot to lead her team to victory.

The first paragraph is like many of the news stories you've written so far. It gives all the facts in a few sentences so the reader quickly understands what happened. The second paragraph, though, was probably more interesting to you than the first. Why is that? The writer reported all the same information, didn't he? What is the major difference between the two paragraphs?

The difference is   THE HOOK

A hook is used to catch fish. In writing, a "hook" is an opening sentence that grabs the reader and pulls him or her into the story. Of course, it isn't painful. Most readers don't mind getting "caught." Writers who know about "hooks" often spend more thought on the opening sentence than on any other part of the story.

With this in mind, go back to the sports story you began on the previous page. If you followed instructions, your paragraph contains all the basic information. But you could probably improve the story with an interesting "hook."

Below are some suggestions for how to do this. Notice that all of the examples answer at least one of the Five-W questions.

1. Start with a quote.	"It was the toughest fight of our lives," remarked Coach Tom Steele of the Valley View Greens.
2. Start with an exclamation.	Ping! Zing! Thump! With a single two-point shot, Terry Smith of the Valley View Greens zapped her team to first place.
3. Start with a question.	Why did fans of the Valley View Greens leave the Hotel Majestic on Friday night with big smiles?
4. Start in the middle of the action.	Tension reigned in the Grand Ballroom of the Hotel Majestic . .

STEP THREE. Rewrite the first paragraph in your sports story with an interesting "hook." Make sure that the information in the paragraph still answers the first four "W" questions.

_____

_____

_____

_____

_____

_____

That was a lot of time spent on one sentence, but it was worth it.

STEP FOUR. Complete the story by writing another paragraph of four to five sentences. Explain **How** and **Why** the winners won (or the losers lost!).

_____

_____

_____

_____

(continued on next page)

_____

_____

I COMPLETED THIS ASSIGNMENT ON _____.

Now that you know how to write a sports story, write another in your notebook. This may be about a game you played or a game you watched. Remember, we're interested in all kinds of sports! Your story should be organized like this:

> First Paragraph--
> > The "hook."
> > Answers to Who, What, When, and Where.
> Second Paragraph--
> > Answers to Why and How

I COMPLETED THIS ASSIGNMENT ON _____.

IMAGINATION STRETCHER

Write a "sports" story about a board game, like Monopoly or Chutes and Ladders. Imagine that the board is bigger than a football field, and you and your friends are the pieces moving around it. Since the story is only a couple of paragraphs long, you should concentrate only on the winning play, and make it exciting!

I COMPLETED THIS ASSIGNMENT ON _____.

REPORTERS FILL IN BLANKS

We have a tough assignment for you. Starting on the next page are three pictures without a story--it's your job to write one. This will take imagination, thought, and all the skills you've been learning. Take your time, and be sure to complete all the steps. Ready?

Do steps 1-3 in the book:

> 1. Think about what is happening in the picture.
> 2. Fill in the "Five-W" chart.
> 3. Write an opening "hook."

Do steps 4-7 in your notebook:

> 4. Copy your opening sentence and complete the first paragraph answering **Who, What, When**, and **Where**.
> 5. Tell **How** and **Why** in the second paragraph.
> 6. Include at least one quote (in quotation marks).
> 7. Write the headline.

PICTURE #1

WHO:
WHAT:
WHEN:
WHERE:
WHY:
HOW:

Opening Sentence: _____

_____

I COMPLETED STEPS 1-3 ON _____.

I COMPLETED STEPS 4-7 ON _____.

PICTURE #2 ("W" chart on next page)

WHO:	WHAT:
WHEN:	WHERE:
WHY:	
HOW:	

Opening Sentence: _____

_____

I COMPLETED STEPS 1-3 ON _____.

I COMPLETED STEPS 4-7 ON _____.

PICTURE #3

WHO:	WHAT:
WHEN:	WHERE:
WHY:	
HOW:	

Opening Sentence: _____

_____

I COMPLETED STEPS 1-3 ON _____.

I COMPLETED STEPS 4-7 ON _____.

For the next story, our readers would like to know more about you!

In the space below, paste a recent snapshot of yourself taken at an event you remember well: the Science Fair, Track and Field Day, Christmas morning or the time you won the Pinewood Derby. If you can't find a photo you like, then think of something that happened to you lately and draw an illustration in the space. Write a news story about the picture, following the steps on page 103.

Do not use the word "I" in your story. Remember, you're the reporter. You must write about yourself *as if* you were someone else. But be sure you don't forget who you are!

| WHO: |
| WHAT: |
| WHEN: |
| WHERE: |
| WHY: |
| HOW: |
| |
| |

_____

_____

_____

_____

_____

_____

_____

_____

_____

_____

(continued on next page)

_____

_____

_____

_____

_____

I COMPLETED THIS ASSIGNMENT ON _____.

INVESTIGATORS GO STRAIGHT TO SOURCE

Until now, you've been writing articles "out of your head." That is, you remembered the facts (or made them up) and then organized them in sentences and paragraphs. But what if we asked you to write a story on a subject you know nothing about? You would have to go find the facts before you could write about them--and that is what reporters do.

Where can facts be found? Open your eyes and look around! Do you see any books? any magazines? a radio? a television? another person? All of these can be sources of information, although they may not always be completely reliable. Here's a good rule to remember when gathering information: in general, the better you know your source, the more you should be able to trust it. Believe what your parents tell you, but don't believe everything the TV tells you!

One of the most popular features of our newspaper is the "Days Gone By" column. Readers enjoy the short stories about our town in the past, such as how the park got its name, why the first automobile was banned, and who got the first parking ticket after parking meters were installed. Almost all our information for this column comes from people who remember the "old days."

We call these people "oral sources" ("oral" comes from the Latin word for "mouth"). They talk about their recollections while the reporter takes notes. Later the reporter puts the story in written form.

Your next assignment is to do some oral research about you. No, you won't have to talk to yourself! We want a story about something you did when you were too young to remember. The best source of information for that would be your parents, grandparents, or older brothers or sisters.

Ask one of these people to spend about half an hour with you, and find a quiet place to sit and talk. You will need a flat surface for taking notes. When the two of you are comfortable, ask your source to recall one of the following occasions:

A time when you embarrassed him or her
A time you said something funny
A time you said something especially cute
A time you called attention to yourself
A time you made him or her proud

While your source is thinking, prepare yourself to take notes.

Note-taking is a skill that gets easier with practice. You can't just listen to what's being said; you must listen *actively*, always asking yourself, "What's most important about what I'm hearing?"

You will write down only the most important points, and *not* in complete sentences. You will probably have to ask your source to stop for a moment while you write something down, and you may have to ask questions to draw out all the facts you need. Remember that all you are doing here is gathering information-- don't try to write your story at the same time!

Here is an example of the notes for a recent "Days Gone By" story. Study it carefully to get an idea of how your notes should read. Later we'll see how notes can be turned into a news story.

NOTES

SOURCE: *Dad*	DATE: *April 8*
WHERE (did this happen)?	
at church (Abundant Life Fellowship)	
WHEN (season, special day, how old I was, etc.)	
Sunday morning worship – 5 yrs. old	
WHO (was involved in this incident)?	
Sarah (me), Ben, Mom, Dad (Mr. & Mrs. David Clark)	
WHAT (happened--main point)?	
D. took S. out of church – everybody heard what she said	
HOW (did this happen)?	
S. teasing B. – Mom said "Stop." S. took B's toy–he cries	
D. mad – taking S. out – just before door – "I object!"	
WHY (did I do this)?	
scared – S. remembered "Perry Mason" shows	
WHY (do you remember this)?	
whole church laughed – D. embarrassed	

When your source is ready to talk, make sure your pencil is sharp and your brain is ready to listen. As he or she tells the story, fill in the answers to the questions below.

NOTES

SOURCE:	DATE:
WHERE (did this happen)?	
WHEN (season, special day, how old I was, etc.)?	
WHO (was involved in this incident)?	
HOW (did this happen)?	
WHY (did I do this)?	
WHY (do you remember this)?	

I COMPLETED THESE NOTES ON _____.

Before you start writing your own story, compare the article below with the notes in our example on page 108. It will help you see how all the information gathered can be expressed in complete sentences and logical paragraphs.

Mr. David Clark still remembers how a quiet little girl broke up the worship one Sunday morning five years ago. Mr. and Mrs. Clark were sitting in the sanctuary of Abundant Life Fellowship with their 5-year-old daughter Sarah and 2-year-old son Ben. Ben was on his mother's lap while Sarah was between her parents.

Sarah, who is usually a very good little girl, was teasing her little brother. She kept it up even after her mother told her to stop. Then she grabbed a toy from Ben and he began to cry. Angrily, Mr. Clark took Sarah's hand and started pulling her down the aisle. Sarah knew she was in trouble and was very scared. Just as they reached the door she said loudly, "I object!"

This was something she had heard watching "Perry Mason" shows on TV. "Perry Mason" is one of her mom's favorite shows and they're always saying, "I object!" in the courtroom. Everyone in the church heard it, and they all broke out laughing! Mr. Clark was <u>very</u> embarrassed, but later he thought it was funny, too.

Now it's time for you to write your story. Your notes will help you remember all the facts as you write. Another thing to remember is not to use the word "I." As you did with the story about the photograph on p. 106, write about yourself as if you were somebody else.

The first paragraph should begin with an interesting "hook" and answer the first four questions on your note page. It should also reveal your source by name (that is, tell where you got your information). Study how the first paragraph of our example accomplished all this, then write your own.

_____

_____

_____

_____

_____

_____

_____

_____

The second paragraph will answer "How?" by telling, in 4-6 sentences, what happened. Refer to your notes so you don't leave anything out.

_____

_____

_____

_____

_____

_____

_____

Now we'll add a third paragraph. This one will answer the two "Why?" questions. You probably don't remember exactly why you did what you did, but your source should have an idea. Be sure to include a statement explaining how your source felt about the incident. This will form the conclusion to your story.

_____

_____

_____

_____

_____

_____

_____

I COMPLETED THIS ASSIGNMENT ON _____.

Good work! Write one more article for the "Days Gone By" column. Your only requirements are that the story must be about something that happened at least five years ago, and you must get your information from an oral source. Here are some suggestions:

Ask a grandparent about something unusual your mother or father
   did when very young.
Ask a neighbor about the people who used to live in your house.
Ask an elderly friend about an interesting knickknack in his or her
   home.

Choose your source, ask your questions, and make your notes in the box below:

NOTES

WHO (was involved)?

WHERE (did this take place)?

WHEN (did this happen)?

WHAT (happened)?

HOW (did this happen)?

WHY (did it happen)?

I COMPLETED THESE NOTES ON _____ .

In your notebook, write a three-paragraph story following this outline:

First Paragraph--Opening "hook" and answer to Who,
      What, Where and When
Second Paragraph--Answer to How
Third Paragraph--Answer to Why

I COMPLETED THIS ASSIGNMENT ON _____ .

IMAGINATION STRETCHER

Your "source" for the next story will be a fictional character--someone in a book or movie who doesn't exist in the real world. Make a note-taking chart similar to the one on page 112. Pretend you are asking your "source" about something that happened to him or her in the book or movie. Or, for a **real** imagination stretcher, fill in details of something that happened right after the book or movie ended.

After you have your notes, write the story according to the outline at the bottom of page 112.

I COMPLETED THE NOTES ON _____.

I COMPLETED THE ASSIGNMENT ON _____.

NEW FACE ON OP-ED PAGE

MEMO

To: All new writers

From: The Editor

You've had experience in just about every area of newspaper writing. There's just one place where your work has not appeared: the Op-Ed section.

"Op-Ed" stands for opinion and Editorial. Most of the newspaper is supposed to be factual reporting - just the news, not how we feel about the news. But on the Op-Ed Page, readers and writers can express their opinions, through letters and editorials.

Speaking of the Op-Ed page, I'm on my way to Hawaii for a vacation. You get to write the editorials this week. Good luck!

That was rather sudden, wasn't it? We'd better waste no time learning to write editorials.

It's important to understand the difference between **fact** and **opinion**. A **factual** statement simply tells us what happened. You've written lots of factual paragraphs in this book. Here's an example:

        Little Veronica Plemmons, 18 months old, was
    named Most Beautiful Baby during the Frontier Days
    Celebration last week. The annual contest was
    held at Founder's Park during the community
    picnic. The beaming beauty won a year's supply of
    baby food, a five-foot teddy bear and a $100
    savings bond. Proud parents are Mr. and Mrs.
    Horace W. Plemmons of Maple Grove.

As long as the facts are correct, no one could argue with that paragraph. But here's an **editorial** based on the same event:

        Veronica Plemmons may be the fairest of them
    all, but the other 27 entries in the Most
    Beautiful Baby Contest are just as beautiful in
    the eyes of their own parents. People are far too
    concerned about outward appearances as it is. Why
    must we start judging our children's physical
    beauty while they're still in diapers? Let's stop
    rewarding shallow values with silly contests.

Some people will agree with this writer. Others will think that she's a spoilsport. It's clear, though, that the writer is not just reporting facts. She is also stating an *opinion* about the facts.

Almost every opinion piece brings up some kind of problem. It might be a small problem, like the shortage of parking spaces at the Little League ballpark, or a huge one, like world hunger. The writer wants to encourage people to think about the problem.

But the writer should also have a solution to propose. The solution to the parking problem at the ballpark is simple: add more spaces. Solving world hunger is not simple at all, but everyone could do something to help: give money to a relief organization, volunteer at a Salvation Army kitchen, or collect canned goods for the food drive at your church.

You will be writing an editorial about a problem that concerns you. Since editorials are a little different from the articles you've written so far, we'll work through an example first.

STEP ONE. Suppose you are concerned about children being hurt on a local playground because the equipment is unsafe. Since the purpose of an opinion piece is to make the reader think, the entire first paragraph should be a "hook."

You might start with a shocking fact:

Last year, four children who went to play at Larkmoor Park ended up in the hospital.

Or you could ask your reader a series of questions:

Aren't playgrounds places where children can go to have fun? Is it too much to ask that they be safe, too?

One of the most effective ways to start an opinion piece is with an example, or a little story:

Kahreem Gullian, age 5, whooped with joy as he swung from the very top bar of the jungle gym. But his laughter turned to screams when the bar broke in his hands and he fell to the hard ground four feet below. His broken arm had to be set in the Emergency Room at Children's Memorial Hospital.

STEP TWO. Now that you have the reader's attention, you must explain your concern clearly. That will be the purpose of the second paragraph--not only to explain the problem, but to include enough facts to prove that it *is* a problem.

Last year, four children were injured so badly at Larkmoor Park that they had to go to the hospital. No one knows how many others went home with bumps, cuts and bruises. It's not hard to find the causes--just go and look at the equipment. Besides the uncut bolts, several bars on the jungle gym are rusty and loose. One of the teeter-totters is not even fastened down. Falls on the rough blacktop are twice as painful as landing on grass or sand would be.

STEP THREE. We should not bring up a problem unless we have a solution! The third paragraph will state what our solution is:

Larkmoor Park has not been kept up the way it should. The City Council should be informed of this problem, so that some of our tax money can be used to buy new equipment and resurface the playground. If there is no money in the city budget for this project, then perhaps we should consider closing the playground.

STEP FOUR. The fourth and last paragraph is probably the most important, because it's the last thing we will have an opportunity to say to our reader. People often remember the last word. For that reason, it's usually best to make the closing paragraph short (no more than two sentences).

It's our business to protect our children. Something must be done about Larkmoor Park.

Are you ready to try it?

Think about something on your street or in your own house that bothers you. Why is this a problem? What can be done? After thinking about it, fill in the chart below.

PROBLEM:
WHY THIS IS A PROBLEM (give two or three reasons why you're concerned)
SOLUTION (tell what you or others can do to solve it)

Since you've put in your "thought time," the editorial shouldn't be too hard to write. Follow this outline for each of your paragraphs:

1. The Hook
2. Statement of the problem
   a. supporting fact
   b. supporting fact
   c. supporting fact (no more than three)
3. Statement of the solution
4. Concluding thought

Paragraph 1:

_____

_____

_____

_____

_____

Paragraph 2:

_____

_____

(continued on next page)

_____

_____

_____

_____

_____

Paragraph 3:

_____

_____

_____

_____

_____

Paragraph 4:

_____

_____

_____

_____

I COMPLETED THIS ASSIGNMENT ON _____.

The editorial you just wrote might also be called an **essay**. An essay is simply a piece that expresses the writer's feelings or opinion about a subject. The outline on page 116 is not the only essay form, but it's a good one to learn.

Think of something that concerns you about your city, state or country. It must be an issue that affects other people besides just your family or close neighbors. Fill in the chart below.

PROBLEM:
WHY THIS IS A PROBLEM (two or three reasons)

(chart continued on next page)

SOLUTION (tell what you or others can do)

I COMPLETED THIS EXERCISE ON _____.

In your notebook, write an editorial about this subject in three paragraphs. Follow the outline on page 116.

I COMPLETED THIS EXERCISE ON _____.

Now we'll do something a little different. Check your second editorial carefully for spelling or other errors, and ask your teacher to read it, too. Then copy the entire piece neatly on clean notebook paper or stationery. Write "Dear Editor" on the top line of the paper. At the end of the editorial write "Sincerely," and sign your name. Write your age below your name. Now your editorial looks like a letter, and so it is--a letter to the editor

Mail the letter to your local newspaper. You should find an address on the Op-Ed page. Watch the paper (or ask friends to watch if your family doesn't subscribe to the paper). If you've done a good job, don't be surprised to see your letter printed!

I COMPLETED THIS ASSIGNMENT ON _____.

YOUNG WRITERS FACE NEW CHALLENGES

You've reached the end of the book, but it will not be the end of your writing career. Have you ever thought about editing your own newspaper? With all your experience, you'd be a natural!

Consider starting a newspaper project with your family, friends, club or neighborhood. Think of an interesting name for your paper and design a **masthead**--that's the heading that appears at the top of the newspaper's front page. Then enlist some help: reporters to contribute articles, advisors to help you make decisions, and a grownup to make photocopies for you. It would also be nice, though not necessary, to have someone type all the articles so they are easy to read.

Your paper could include sports stories, news briefs, comics, classifieds, editorials, and much more of interest to your community. Weekly papers are a lot of work; we would suggest a monthly at first.

But even if you don't start a newspaper, you'll be able to use your writing skills for years to come. Keep practicing, and keep learning!

A N S W E R S

PAGE	QUESTION NUMBER AND ANSWER

12   A2 plant, flower, rose
      3 toy - ball, baseball
      4 food, fruit, pear
      5 dish, cup, mug
      6 desert, cake, cupcake

12   B1 convertable
      2 drapes
      3 pine

16   Rules For A Cinquain-like Poem

> 1. Five lines long
> 2. Begins and ends with a noun which is repeated (though perhaps in a different way on the last line)
> 3. Lines 2, 3 & 4 are each progressively longer, but line 5 is short

20   Verbs - baking, decorating, sweeping, apply, ask, involves, dusting, vacuuming, cooking, reading

28   1. Compound object
      2. Compound predicate
      3. Compound subject
      4. Compound verb
      5. Compound subject
      6. Compound object

36   1. MAYOR | ORDERS INVESTIGATION

      2. RECORD SNOWS | FORCE SCHOOLS TO CLOSE

      3. FAITHFUL DOG | DRIVES OFF ATTACKER AND SAVES OWNER

      4. SEVEN STUDENTS | ON HONOR ROLL

41   1. pretty 2. red-headed, friendly 3. pleased, upset 4. handsome, bashful
      5. noisy

73   The first meeting of . . .
      After much discussion . . .
      All of these are services . . .
      All interested citizens . . .

B

| PAGE | QUESTION NUMBER AND ANSWER |

74   2. Tickets were $1.50 in advance . . .
75   3. Rock pythons are native to . . .
        4. The "Holiday in Lights" winter show . . .

75   2. To describe the good qualities of a play
        3. To tell a story
        4. To convince the reader

77   The rearranged sentences should be in this order:

The Kennel Club pet show was a howling success, but not in the way its sponsors intended. The Armory Hall resounded to the barks of over one hundred entries. Dogs of 37 different breed participated in the show. Huskies, mastiffs, and Indian dholes were some of the many breeds observed by this reporter. Anxious owners groomed their pets, each hoping to take home the $150 grand prize.

Some practical joker set a rabbit loose on the viewing stage during the final judging. The frightened bunny leapt off the viewing stage and tore down the nearest aisle, followed by three prize pups. The dogs who could not join the chase added their voices to the tremendous din. A quick-thinking custodian scooped the rabbit into a cardboard box and out of harm's way. After all the excitement, Miss Mange, a Llasa Apso, was awarded Best of Show.

78   The rearranged sentences should be in this order:

Young Jim Martins is now known as a hero to his neighbors on 27th Ave. Last week, he was just the paper boy. This week, he can't complete his route without people stopping him to ask about the burning home.

Just before dawn on Wednesday, Jim Martins was completing his route on 99th Street. Suddenly, he smelled a whiff of smoke. Peering at the nearest duplex, he thought he saw a reflection of flames on a wall. Jim jumped off his bike and raced to the door of the duplex. He pounded on the door but received no answer, so he broke the front window and entered the apartment.

Minnie Page, the 76-year-old resident, was asleep in her bedroom. The smoke alarm had failed to go off, due to a dead battery. Jim woke her and led her to safety just moments before she would have succumbed to smoke inhalation. "He saved my life," Mrs. Page said later. "I can't thank God enough that Jim was there."

85   Best synopses: THE THREE BEARS, #2; DAVID & GOLIATH, #3